While every care has been taken in the compiling of information contained in this volume, the publisher cannot accept liability for loss, financial or otherwise, incurred by reliance placed on the information herein.

The publishers wish to express their sincere thanks to the following for their involvement and assistance in the production of this volume:

Editor: Tony Curtis
Photographer: Phillip Springthorpe
Foreword: Eelin McIvor
Editorial: Annette Curtis
                 Catriona Day
                 Donna Cruickshank
                 Angela De Marco
                 Donna Rutherford
                 Jacqueline Leddy
                 James Brown
                 Nicky Fairburn
                 Frank Burrell
                 Tim Barnard (Airbrush Retoucher)

A CIP catalogue record for this book is available from the British Library.

ISBN 86248-146-5

Copyright © Lyle Publications MCMXCIII
Glenmayne, Galashiels, Scotland

Typeset by Word Power, Coldingham, Berwickshire.
Printed and bound in Great Britain by
Butler & Tanner Ltd., Frome and London.

A Fortune in your Attic

in your

Attic

Tony Curtis

Acknowledgements

Auction Team Köln, Postfach 50 11 68, D-5000 Köln 50, Germany.
Christopher Baglee Style Collection, 16 Eastcliffe Avenue,
Newcastle Upon Tyne, NE3 4SN.
R. Bannister, Cowleigh Bank, Malvern, Worcestershire.
Brian Bates, Fairview, Maer, Newcastle, Staffs.
Bonhams, Montpelier Street, Knightsbridge, London SW7 1HH.
Bonhams Chelsea, 65–69 Lots Road, London SW10 0RN
Christie's Scotland, 164-166 Bath Street, Glasgow G2 4TG.
Christie's South Kensington Ltd., 85 Old Brompton Road, London SW7 3LD.
Christie's, 8 King Street, London SW1Y 6QT.
Christie's East, 219 East 67th Street, New York, NY 10021, USA.
Nic Costa, 166 Camden Street, London NW1 9PT.
George Court, 48a Bridge Street, Leominster, Herefordshire HR6 8DZ.
Finarte, 20121 Milano, Piazzetta Bossi 4, Italy.
The Goss & Crested China Co., 62 Murray Road, Horndean, Hants PO8 9JL.
Greenslade Hunt, 13 Hammet Street, Taunton, Somerset, TA1 1RN.
Muir Hewitt, Halifax Antiques Centre, Queens Road/Gibbet Street, Halifax HX1
4LR.
Hilary Humphries, The Cigarette Packet Collectors Club, 15 Dullingham Road,
Newmarket, Suffolk CB8 9JT.
Jacobs & Hunt, Lavant Street, Petersfield, Hants.
W.H. Jones, Ferndale, Stanner Road, Kington, HR5 3NL.
Lawrence Fine Art, South Street, Crewkerne, Somerset, TA18 8AB.
Dave Lewis Art Studio, 20 The Avenue, Starbeck, Harrogate,
North Yorkshire HG1 4QD.
The Period Petrol Pump Co., The, Grove Farm, Mill Green, Burston, Diss,
Norfolk.
Phillips, 65 George Street, Edinburgh EH2 2JL.
Phillips, Blenstock House, 7 Blenheim Street, New Bond Street,
London W1Y 0AS.
Sheffield Railwayana Auctions, 43 Little Norton Lane, Sheffield S8 8GA.
Paul Sheppard, The Vallets, Forge Crossing, Lyonshall, Kington, Herefordshire.
Skinner Inc., Bolton Gallery, Route 117, Bolton MA, USA.
Sotheby's, 34-35 New Bond Street, London W1A 2AA.
Sotheby's, 1334 York Avenue (at 72nd Street), New York, NY 10021, USA.
Paul Spindley, 14 Horncastle Road, Louth, Lincs, LN11 9LD.
Street Jewellery, 16 Eastcliffe Avenue, Newcastle Upon Tyne NE3 4SN.
G.E. Sworder & Son, Northgate End Salerooms, 15 Northgate End, Bishop
Stortford, Herts.
Tennants, 27 Market Place, Leyburn, Yorkshire.
Ute Twite, Togford, Stogumber, Taunton, Somerset TA4 3TN.
T. Vennett Smith, 11 Nottingham Road, Gotham, Nottingham NG11 0HE.
Sam Weller, The Old Curiosity Shop, Old Railway Station, Reepham, Norfolk.
Yesterday's Paper, Ivybank House, 122 Upgate, Louth, Lincolnshire LN11 9HG.

Contents

Trash or Treasure?

You'd think it would be getting more and more difficult by now to find that Fortune in Your Attic, with so many enthusiastic and clued-up viewers of the Antiques Road Show, and the vast amount of other publicity on the subject which bombards us daily in just about every paper and magazine. Not a bit of it, however! There's still hardly a week goes by without news of some amazing find or other. One of the most delightful of recent days was the Meléndez Still Life sold by Bonhams for £850,000. The seller had purchased it thirty years ago for a few shillings in a street market as a photographic print!

Such things don't turn up every day, it's true, but there are plenty of other more everyday items which will also fetch a very tidy sum. Film posters, for example, are a burgeoning market, especially when they feature popular stars such as Charlie Chaplin. One of his major films was 'The Circus', dating from 1928, and a poster for this has fetched £11,968 at Christie's.

Luis Meléndez – 'A still life of sea bream, oranges, garlic, a cloth and kitchen utensils on a wooden table' – signed and dated 1772 – oil on canvas – 41 x 62.8cm.
(Bonhams)   *£850,000*

Then just about everyone has a few Dinky toys stashed away somewhere which are becoming ever more sought after. If you can also boast some early German Märklin models, however, a Grand Station or an electric liner, for example, then we're talking serious money.

Marklin electric, 'Kaiser Wilhelm Der Grosse', circa 1909, 117cm. long. This model was the largest Marklin liner and would run with two 4 volt batteries for seven hours. (Christie's S.Ken)   £33,000

Marklin, Grand Station, with track, canopy, interior and exterior fittings, working clocks and electric lighting, circa 1909, 92cm. wide, 54cm. high.
(Christie's) £16,500

Also, the scope of what is potentially valuable is extending all the time. Items which were on the periphery of collectables only a couple of years ago have now moved firmly into the mainstream, and many others are poised to follow them. When Christie's decide that it's worthwhile devoting a sale to old gas cookers, you realise just what unlikely things can now be worth surprising sums.

So make an even more ruthless appraisal of what you've got stashed away. Odds are, if you've kept it, it must be of some interest to you, and the chances are that there are other like-minded people out there who share your enthusiasm. For make no mistake, the more people who are interested in any range of items, the faster their value will rise, whether it be beer mats or bicycles, cigarette cards or soup can labels.

Most fun of all to collect are probably those items that you can pick up for a song before most other people catch on to them. There are, of course, no certainties in the collecting world, and nothing is guaranteed to rise in value, but then the uncertainty itself is part of the buzz. (If you like, and are genuinely interested in what you collect, for its own sake, however, you can't go far wrong.)

A Fortune in Your Attic will provide an invaluable update on just what is fetching money today, and what could well be fetching similar sums tomorrow. So take another hard look at the contents of your garage, loft, garden shed or wherever. There's a whole lot of treasure out there still!

Aeronautica

The honour of being first in the air belongs to America – the first aeroplane was invented by Samuel Pierpoint Langley in 1896 and the first powered flight was made in 1903 by the Wright brothers. Since those early days enthusiasts have vied to possess relics of flight and books, photographs, log books, airmail letters, posters and even bits of old planes are collected. The field is enormous, ranging from autographs or photographs of flying aces like Amy Johnston and Jim Mollison, Douglas Bader, Sheila Scott or space age astronauts to ashtrays and cigarette lighters made in the shape of aeroplanes or zeppelins.

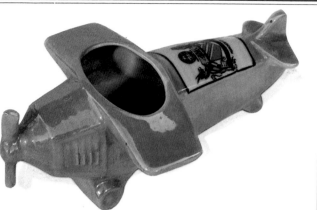

Crested Ware Aeroplane, circa 1930. £30

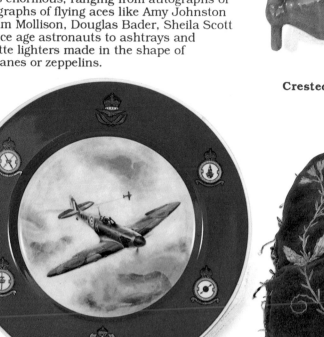

Royal Worcester commemorative plate for the 50th anniversary of the **Battle of Britain**, boxed limited edition. £45

Royal Air Force Tea Cosy, **Squadron 37**, embroidery on velvet. £20

World War 2 Flying Helmet complete with strap. £50

World War 2 sextant in a fitted bakelite case. £70

(George Court)

Aeronautica

Scrap albums for **Air Pioneer Captain Longcroft**, 1913. £200

Astro Compass MK II from a World War 2 bomber. £50

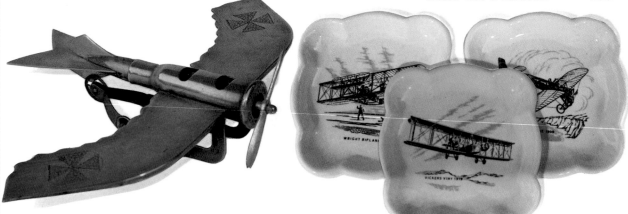

Trench Art German Aircraft, World War 1. £70

Wade set of three porcelain plates, **'Famous Aircraft'**, 1959. £33

Wooden casket made from a propeller, World War 1. £15

Joystick from a crashed bi-plane at Burton-on-Trent, 1910, flown by **Laborie**, with accompanying album. £100

(George Court)

Aeronautica

The Spitfire Mug by **Wedgwood**, limited edition of 200, 1969. £200

First World War Trench Art Aeroplane, made to be a car mascot. £80

Wooden cased clock made from propeller timber, World War 1. £70

Royal Air Force cap badge. £5

Royal Worcester commemorative plate for the 50th anniversary of the **Battle of Britain**. £45

Shell aviation fuel can complete with filler tube. £40

(George Court)

Aeronautica

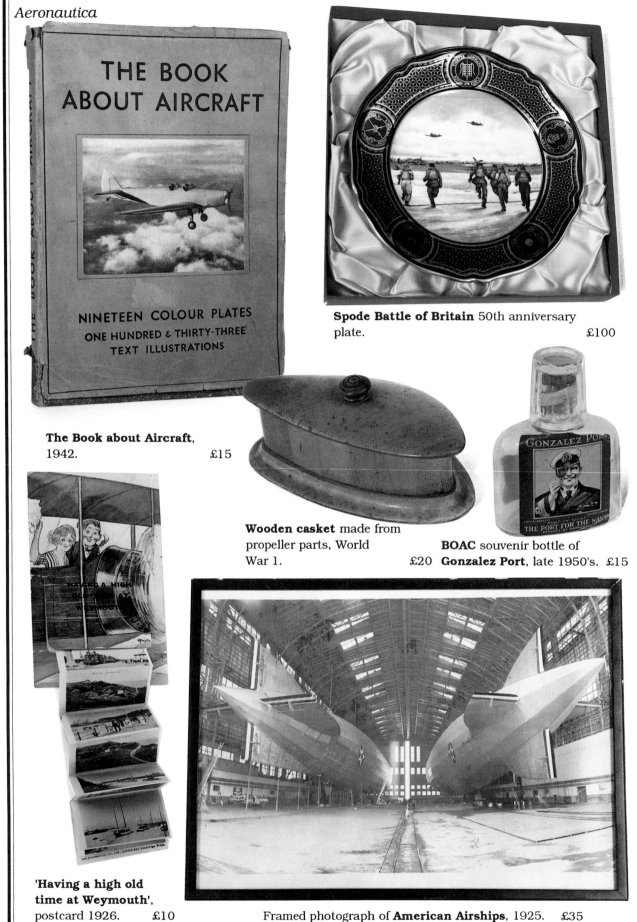

THE BOOK ABOUT AIRCRAFT

NINETEEN COLOUR PLATES
ONE HUNDRED & THIRTY-THREE TEXT ILLUSTRATIONS

Spode Battle of Britain 50th anniversary plate.   £100

The Book about Aircraft, 1942.   £15

Wooden casket made from propeller parts, World War 1.   £20

BOAC souvenir bottle of **Gonzalez Port**, late 1950's. £15

'Having a high old time at Weymouth', postcard 1926.   £10

Framed photograph of **American Airships**, 1925.   £35

(George Court)

Aeronautica

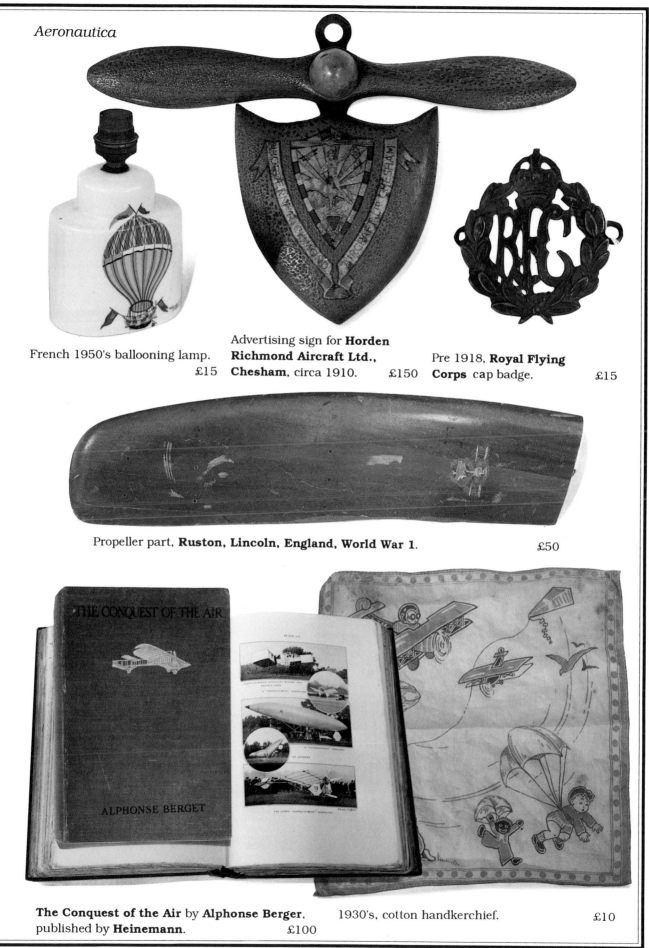

French 1950's ballooning lamp. £15

Advertising sign for **Horden Richmond Aircraft Ltd., Chesham**, circa 1910. £150

Pre 1918, **Royal Flying Corps** cap badge. £15

Propeller part, **Ruston, Lincoln, England, World War 1**. £50

The Conquest of the Air by **Alphonse Berger**, published by **Heinemann**. £100

1930's, cotton handkerchief. £10

(George Court)

Amusement Machines

Egyptian Bell, made in the U.K., circa 1932.
(Costa/Bates)   £2,000

Tote Winna amusement machine, electrical
mechanical version, 1950's, 28in. high.
(Sam Weller)   £200

Beromat Fruit Machine by **G.A. Whittaker Ltd.**,
Blackpool, 28in. high, 1974. (Sam Weller)   £200

Rol-a-Top, produced by **Watling** with twin
jackpot, made in the U.S.A., circa 1936.   £2,000

Amusement Machines

Jennings Governor Fruit Machine, late 1950's, 29in. high.
(Paul Spindley)   £600

Dr Bones X-Ray machine, circa 1950, U.K.
(Costa/Bates)   £250

Elevenses, circa 1955, U.K.
(Costa/Bates)   £250

Egg Laying Hen made by C.F. Schulze & Co.,
Berlin.   (Auction Team Koln)   £2,474

Amusement Machines

1930's wooden cased amusement machine in the **Art Deco** style.   £450

War Eagle, produced by **Mills** in the U.S.A., circa 1932.   £1,200

Sky Jump, circa 1948, made in the U.K.   £220

Pussy Shooter, made by the **British American Novelty Co.**, U.K., circa 1930.   £1,500

Floodlit Football amusement machine by **Kay**, 1950's, 19³/₄in. long. (Sam Weller)   £20

Buckley Digger, made in the U.S.A., circa 1934.   £2,000

(Costa/Bates)

A Fortune in your Attic

Autographs

One of the problems with autographed photographs is deciding whether the signature is genuine. During the boom years of the cinema, when fans in their thousands would write demanding signed pictures of their idols, the studios employed Press Officers to despatch and often forge the signature on these themselves. Even politicians such as Churchill sometimes employed writing machines to forge their signatures, though these can be fairly easily detected. If a signature can be proved genuine, the price obviously soars, and a personal dedication or message is invaluable here. Pictures from the early years of the art, before commercialism set in, say of Tchaikowsky or Queen Victoria will also usually fetch more.

Batman & Robin, signed photograph, 8 x 10in., **Adam West and Burt Ward**. £35

Alfred Hitchcock signed receipt from **Paramount Pictures, Inc.**, 19th May 1958. £200

Cindy Crawford, signed photograph, 8 x 10in. £40

(T. Vennett Smith)

Autographs

Bela Lugosi as **Dracula**, signed photograph.

£300

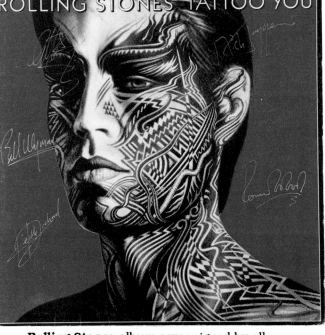

Maurice Ravel, signed letter dated 27.5.21. £500

Enrico Caruso, signed postcard, 1903.   £200

Rolling Stones album cover signed by all members of the group.   £300

(T. Vennett Smith)

Autographs

Winston Churchill cigar bearing the band
'Special for Sir Winston L.S. Churchill'.   £200

Bela Bartok, signed caricature.   £400

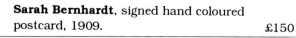

Sarah Bernhardt, signed hand coloured
postcard, 1909.   £150

Montgomery Clift, signed photograph.   £120

(T. Vennett Smith)

Autographs

Big Bopper (J.R. Richardson)
autograph. £800

Steven Spielberg, signed photograph. £60

Greta Garbo autograph, apparently signed to accompany a gift of a **Clarice Cliff** plate to a friend in America in 1962. £500

Stan Laurel and **Oliver Hardy**, signed photograph. £300

Billie Jean King, signed photograph. £15

(T. Vennett Smith)

Autographs

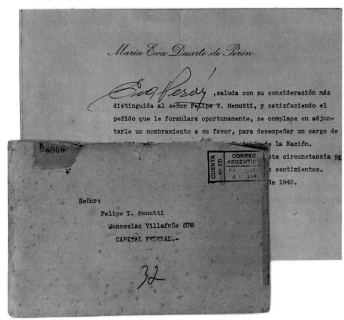

Eva Peron, signed letter of appointment 11th March 1949.   £300

Lloyd George, signed postcard.   £40

Julius Streicher, hanged October 16th, 1946, 7 x 9in.   £500

Ingrid Bergman, signed postcard.   £40

(T. Vennett Smith)

Autographs

Winston Churchill on **Onassis Yacht Christina**, signed photograph a gift to his nurse, 1960's.   £1,000

P.F. Warner, signed photograph, 1912.   £100

Montgomery of Alamein, signed official photograph, 7 x 5in.   £50

(T. Vennett Smith)

A Fortune in your Attic

Autographs

Bob Dylan, signed photograph, 8 x 10in.   £150

The Beatles, publicity photograph signed by all four.   £600

Cary Grant, signed photograph, 8 x 10in.   £90

Winston Churchill, signed photograph, 7 x 5in.   £800

(T. Vennett Smith)

Autographs

Floyd Patterson, signed photograph, 8 x 10in.
£30

Patrick Swayze, signed photograph, 8 x 10in.
£60

Steffi Graf, signed photograph, 8 x 10in.   £30

Bridget Bardot, signed photograph, 8 x 10in.
£50

(T. Vennett Smith)

Automatons

The earliest automatons were devised in the 18th century by a Swiss family called Jacquet-Droz and they were the wonder of the sophisticated world at that time. Some early automatons were made in the form of animal orchestras with monkeys in powdered wigs and silken jackets playing instruments with musical accompaniments, or elegant singing birds in gilded cages, opening their beaks and turning their heads as they poured out their songs. The first automatons were, like watches, powered by ingeniously coiled springs but other inventors propelled their machines with compressed air, water, sand, mercury or steam. It was the spring however that proved to be the most popular.

A musical automaton modelled as a standing **Negro banjo player** by **Vichy**, 18" high. (Christie's) £3,080

A musical automaton of a female flute player, French, last quarter 19th century, 16¹/₂" high. (Tennants) £700

A bisque headed clockwork musical automaton by **Vichy**, circa 1890. (Christie's) £3,520

Fruit Seller, a leather headed clockwork musical automaton by **Vichy**. (Christie's) £8,800

A Negro smoking automaton by **Vichy**. (Christie's S. Ken.) £4,840

25

Avon Bottles

Most women will remember at least some of the pretty and imaginative containers in which the Avon company have marketed their products since their launch on the UK market in the early 60's. To attract top prices, bottles should be in pristine condition, accompanied by original boxes where these existed. Full bottles, however, do not attract a premium.

Tai Winds Aftershave, bloodhound pipe bottle. £8

Aftershave motor bike bottle. £15

Bird of Paradise in blue, **Unforgettable** cologne. £7

Xmas decoration bubble bath oil. £9

Avon Moonwind Pierrot bottle. £6

Charisma Cologne Avonshire blue (Wedgwood copy) £5

Occur eau de Cologne gramophone. £5

Sweet Honesty perfume teddy bear. £5

First Flowers eau de cologne girl with doll, body blue and white head. £8

Moonwind eau de Cologne, gold telephone bottle. £5

Elegance, blue bell bottle. £6

(Paul Sheppard)

Avon Bottles

Tai Winds Aftershave, Dutch pipe bottle. £15

Spicy Aftershave, **Horse**, **'Sport of Kings'**. £8

Hud Aftershave, Viking Discoverer bottle. £25

Exclusive bath oil entura jug. £5

Andy Cap Blue Blazer body powder, 1969. £100

Moonwind bath oil, orange teapot. £8

Nexus Aftershave, footballer bottle. £20

Fragrance Hours Bird of Paradise cologne, longcase clock. £10

First Flowers Cologne, mouse with veil. £9

Imperator Aftershave **Supersleuth** magnifying glass. £15

Lilac Bath Oil **'Little Dutch Kettle'**. £8

Felina Fluffles First Flowers Cologne. £5

(Paul Sheppard)

27

Calendars

Favourite calendars were cherished for years
and some from the 1930's are very collectable,
especially those that offer a nostalgic view of the
past and the countryside. The same kind of
pictures appeared on calendars as on jigsaw
puzzles – gardens full of flowers, ladies in
crinolines gathering blossoms and, a great
favourite, a black dog and a white one
surrounded by sprigs of heather in a Highland
background. The firm of Suttons made some of
the most popular.

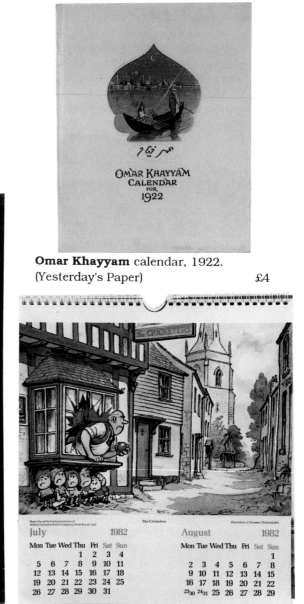

Omar Khayyam calendar, 1922.
(Yesterday's Paper)   £4

The Hobbit calendar, 1976.
(Yesterday's Paper)   £10

Norman Thelwell calendar, 1982.
(Yesterday's Paper)   £3

1930 Novelty calendar, **'Folks hevn't changed much since the good old days'**.
(Yesterday's Paper)   £8

Calendars

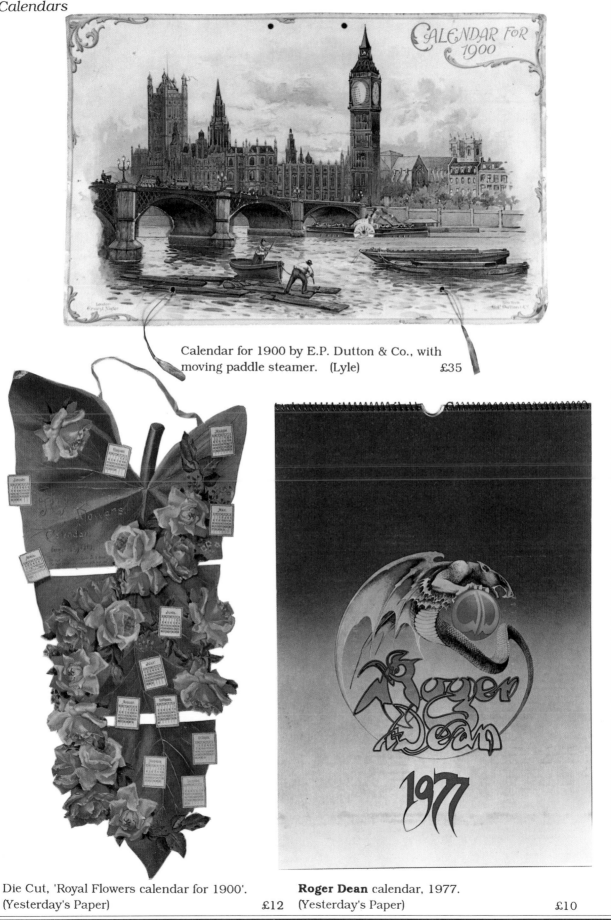

Calendar for 1900 by E.P. Dutton & Co., with
moving paddle steamer.   (Lyle)   £35

Die Cut, 'Royal Flowers calendar for 1900'.
(Yesterday's Paper)   £12

Roger Dean calendar, 1977.
(Yesterday's Paper)   £10

Cameras

A **35mm Leica 250 Reporter FF camera** with a **Leitz Elmar 5cm F/3.5 lens**.
(Christie's)   £3,850

A very rare **35mm black Leica M2-R camera**, No. 1248646.
(Christie's S. Ken.)   £4,180

A **W. Watson & Sons whole plate brass, mahogany and aluminium fitted field camera** with an **aluminium bound Watson lens**.
(Christie's)   £198

A postcard horizontal tropical **Soho reflex camera** by **Marion & Co., London** with polished teak body.
(Christie's)   £1,870

A very rare 2¹/₄ x 3¹/₄ rollfilm **No. 2 Cone Pocket Kodak camera** with Morocco leather covered body. (Christie's S. Ken)   £3,520

A **35mm Black point Nikon S3M camera** with a **Nikon Nikkor-H F/2 5cm. lens**.
(Christie's)   £28,600

Cameras

A very rare decoratively engraved **spy camera**, reputedly used by the **Russian K.G.B.** (Christie's S. Ken.) £12,100

Eastman Kodak Co., Rochester NY, a 120 rollfilm cardboard body **George Washington Kodak camera**. (Christie's) £14,300

A rare and unusual 6^1/$_2$ x 7^1/$_2$in. mahogany **collapsible camera** with brass fittings by **Horne & Thornwaite**. (Christie's) £7,150

A 5 x 4in. mahogany and brass **Sanderson field camera** by **Houghtons Ltd., London**. (Christie's) £605

Marion and Co. Ltd., London, a 140 x 90mm tropical stereoscopic reflex camera with inset brass binding. £4,950

A **35mm walnut bodied Cinematographic camera** with brass body direct vision finder by **Lumiere**. (Christie's) £12,650

A 120 rollfilm prototype **Rolleiflex camera** by **Franke and Heidecke**.(Christie's) £2,860

Character Jugs

The first Royal Doulton Character Jug, titled 'John Barleycorn Old Lad' was produced in the early 1930's from a design and model by Charles Noke. As the popularity of the jugs grew, many new characters were introduced including 'Sairey Gamp', 'Parson Brown', 'Dick Turpin' and 'Old Charley'. Some of these jugs are still in production today but many of the earlier designs were discontinued in the sixties.

One of the first to be withdrawn was the Churchill character jug made during the Battle of Britain and designed as a Loving Cup by C.J. Noke. It is cream coloured with two black handles and bears the inscription 'Winston Churchill Prime Minister of Britain 1940'. It was withdrawn after only eighteen months however because, it is said, Churchill himself was not pleased with the likeness. Because so few were produced this jug is an extremely rare and desirable item, coveted by collectors throughout the world, and a fair estimate of its price at auction today is five thousand pounds.

Clark Gable, D6709.   £2,200   **Maori**, 1939.   £7,500

Touchstone, D5613.   £90   **Smuts**, D6198.   £680

Vicar of Bray, D5615.   £100   **W.C. Fields**, D6674.   £45   **Simon The Cellarer**, D5504. £60

Character Jugs

Pearly Boy (Blue), 1947. £2,250   **Friar Tuck**, D6321.   £180   **Clown** (Red Haired), D5610 £1,250

John Peel, D5612.   £70   **Ugly Duchess**, D6599.   £230   **Cardinal**, D6129.   £70

Jarge, D6288.   £145   **Granny** (Toothless Version),   **Buz Fuz**, D5838.   £85
                                D5521.   £450

Character Jugs

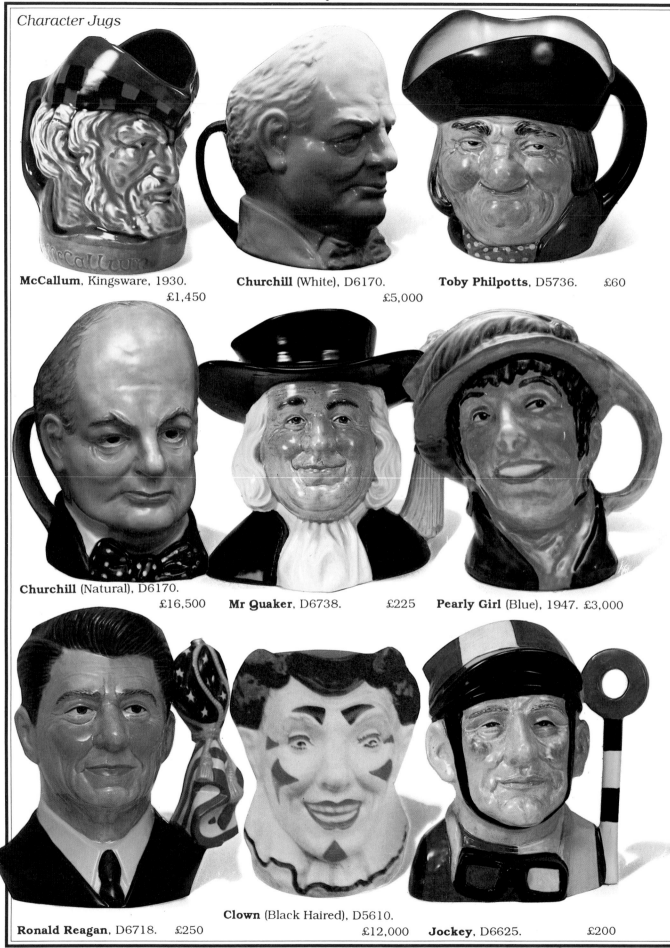

McCallum, Kingsware, 1930.
£1,450

Churchill (White), D6170.
£5,000

Toby Philpotts, D5736.   £60

Churchill (Natural), D6170.
£16,500

Mr Quaker, D6738.   £225

Pearly Girl (Blue), 1947. £3,000

Clown (Black Haired), D5610.

Ronald Reagan, D6718.   £250

£12,000

Jockey, D6625.   £200

Character Jugs

Mephistopheles, D5757. £900   **Uncle Tom Cobbleigh**, D6337.   **John Barleycorn**, D5327.   £70
£170

Fortune Teller, D6497.   £250   **Old King Cole** (Yellow Crown),   **Simple Simon**, D6374.   £260
D6036   £800

Johnny Appleseed, D6372.
£165   **Lord Nelson**, D6336.   £160   **Dick Whittington**, D6375. £160

Childrens Books

Left

The Golliwogg's Airship by **Florence K. Upton**, 1902.   £50

Louis Wain's Summer Book for 1903 published by **Hutchinson & Co.**   £50

Kitty Kat Cartoons by **Dick Hill**, 1950.   £8

The New Rupert Book, 1938.   £150

Three Blind Mice illustrated by **Walton Corbould**.   £15

The Pussy Cat Willum Book, 1962.   £8

(Yesterday's Paper)

Right

H for Harry, The Story of a Hampden Bomber by **Walter & Bridget Moss**, circa 1940.   £12

Tom Puss Tales by **Marten Toonder**, circa 1950.   £40

Beauty and the Beast, Father Tuck's Happy Hour Series, circa 1900.   £20

The Peek-A-Boos in Camp drawn by **Chloe Preston**, circa 1916.   £30

(Yesterday's Paper)

Childrens Books

Guinness give-away, **'Alice where art thou'**, **'What will they think of next'**, A Guinness Sport folio, circa 1950.

£15–25 each

Sexton Blake annual, souvenir of the **Worlds Greatest Detective**. £25

Verbeck's Bears in Mother Goose-Land, by **Hanna Rion**, circa 1915. £35

The Trocious Twins at the Sea, verses by **R. Parker**, illustrated by **N. Parker**, circa 1910. £50

The Story of Babar, 1st edition, 1934. £40

(Yesterday's Paper)

Childrens Books

Railway A.B.C. by Dean & Son. £100

The Magic Beano Book, 1950. £45

Tuck's Toys Rockers cut-out book, circa 1910. £50

Rupert Adventure Series, 1940's, 1950's. £15–£40 each.

Set of four **Rummy Tales** by **Lawson Wood**, 1930's. £20

Childrens Books

Childrens Books

Left

Jalopy 'The Taxi-cab Cat' by **Louis Cochrane**, illustrated by **Elizabeth Jackson**, 1957.   £5

A Nursery Alphabet by **Nelson**, 1930's.   £30

Set of three **Florence Upton Golliwogg** books, circa 1900.   £50

'For Kitty and Me', printed by **Blackie & Sons**, 1907.   £12

A Carol, **Good King Wenceslas** with drawings by **Jessie M. King**.   £65

Right

Orlando and the Three Graces by **Kathleen Hale**, 1965.   £15

Rupert and the Happy Wish, a **Daily Express** Publication, 1950. £20

Our Hospital ABC, pictures by **Joyce Dennys**, verses by **Hampden Gordon** & **M.C. Tindall**, 1916.   £25

Tree Fairies by **Patricia Robins**, illustrated by **Franke Rogers**, 1945.   £15

The Royal Progress of King Pepito Kate Greenaway, 1st edition.   £40

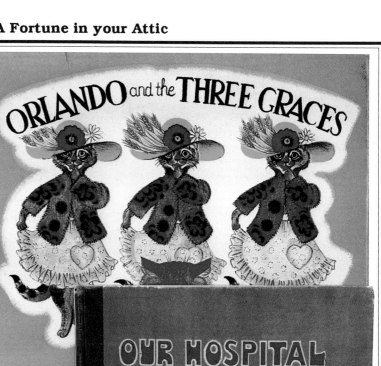

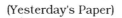

(Yesterday's Paper)

China

Porcelain was introduced into Europe from China in the 16th century and became an instant collectable for moneyed classes. The secrets of its manufacture were discovered in France and Germany in the early 18th century, and during the next few decades the Sevres, Meissen and Dresden factories produced most of the cabinet ware of the period.

1930's **Bunny** teapot. (Muir Hewitt) £110

Pair of late 19th century German nodding figures **Grandma and Grandpa**. (Phillips) £150

Clarice Cliff wall plaque inspired by **Diaghilev's** costume design for the **Ballet Russe**. (Christie's) £8,000

Meissen porcelain coffee pot, 1750, 31cm. high. (Finarte) £21,100

19th century **Blackamoor** figure wearing a wide brimmed straw hat. 2ft. (Greenslades) £950

Meissen figure of a seated ape modelled by **Johann Gottlieb Kirchner**, 1735, (Christie's) £6,600

China

A 1930's novelty three piece pottery tea set.
(Greenslades) £80

A **Meissen Chinoiserie** salt from the **Brühlsche
Plat De Menage** modelled by **J.J. Kändler**,
1737, 19cm. high.
(Christie's) £7,700

Minton Majolica garden seat modelled
as a **Crouching Monkey**, 1870, 47cm.
high. (Christie's) £7,150

A **London Delft** blue dash Royal portrait charger
depicting **Charles II**, circa 1685, 32.5cm.
diameter. (Christie's) £16,500

Pair of **Clarice Cliff** teddy bear book ends, 6in.
high. (Christie's S. Ken.) £4,180

China

19th century **Satsuma** figure of a boy, 38cm. high. (Finarte) £3,400

George Robey Toby Jug by **Doulton**, 1925, 10^{1}/$_{2}$in. high. (Lyle) £3,500

Royal Doulton George Washington Bicentenary jug, 10^{3}/$_{4}$in. high. (Lyle) £4,500

A fine and rare underglaze blue, yellow ground vase, 8in. high. (Christie's) £429,077

A **London Delft** dated candlestick of tapering cylindrical form with wide fluted drip pan, 1653, 25.5cm. high. (Christie's) £154,000

A large and early **Wemyss** model of a pig, 44cm. long. (Phillips) £3,200

China

Pair of **Royal Dux** figures of water
carriers. (Jacobs & Hunt)   £400

A rare **Burleighware** wall plaque with a
design of a galleon in full sail by
Charlotte Rhead.
(Michael Newman)   £940

A **George Jones** majolica bowl
supported by **Mr Punch**. £2,750

An amusing **Martin
Brothers** stoneware
model of a baby owl,
1895, 27.5cm. high.
(Phillips) £3,000

A **Liverpool delft** dated inkpot, 1756,
7cm. diameter. (Christie's)   £16,500

An **English delft** blue and white
drinking vessel modelled as a spurred
boot, 1650, 17.5cm. high.   £12,100

45

Christmas Scraps

Throwing Snowballs,
$9^{1}/_{2}$in. x 4in. £8
Angel with holly,
4in. x $1^{1}/_{2}$in. £3
Christmas Angel,
$5^{1}/_{2}$in. x $2^{1}/_{4}$in. £4
St. Nicholas with children,
9in. x $10^{1}/_{2}$in. £15
St. Nicholas with toys,
$9^{1}/_{2}$in. x $4^{1}/_{4}$in. £15
Girl with Christmas
Pudding, 12in. x $5^{1}/_{2}$in. £18
The Bell Ringer,
3in. x $1^{1}/_{4}$in. £3
(Ute Twite)

Christmas Scraps

Christmas was one of the most popular themes of children's scraps. The scraps had an additional function in that they could be used to decorate the envelope of a Christmas card, or, in some cases where they were big enough, as a Christmas card in themselves.

Angel with drum,
4in. x $1^1/_2$in.   £3
A **Christmas Angel**, bell ringer, 3in. x $1^1/_4$in.   £3
A **Christmas Angel**,
9in. x $3^1/_4$in.   £15
Girl in cloak,
$6^3/_4$in. x $4^1/_2$in.   £4
Carol Singer,
$11^1/_2$in. x 4in.   £12
Angel with muff,
4in. x $1^1/_2$in.   £3
Around the Christmas Tree,
$12^1/_2$in. x $9^1/_4$in.   £30
(Ute Twite)

Cigarette Cards

Cigarette Cards
Cigarette cards were first used as stiffeners in packages of cigarettes in the days before slide packets. They probably made their first appearance in the 1860's in the United States. The oldest card known to exist is in the Metropolitan Museum in New York and dates from 1878. W.D. & H.O. Wills were the first British firm to give away cards with their cigarettes in 1885. Between then and the end of the Second World War more than 5,000 sets of cards were produced.

Kinnear Ltd., Australian Cricketers, 1898, set of 15.
£165 each

Edwards, Ringer & Bigg, Flags of All Nations, 1907, set of 25.
£125

Cohen Weenen & Co., Famous Boxers, 1912, set of 25. £200

Stephen Mitchell & Son, Sports, 1907, set of 25. £250 set

Ogden's Ltd., British Costumes from 100BC to 1904, set of 50. £275 set

J.H. Clure & Son, War Portraits, 1916, set of 50.
£700 set

W.D. & H.O. Wills, Cricketers, 1908, set of 50. £15 each

W.D. & H.O. Wills, Recruiting Posters, 1915, set of 12. £75 set

Cigarette Cards

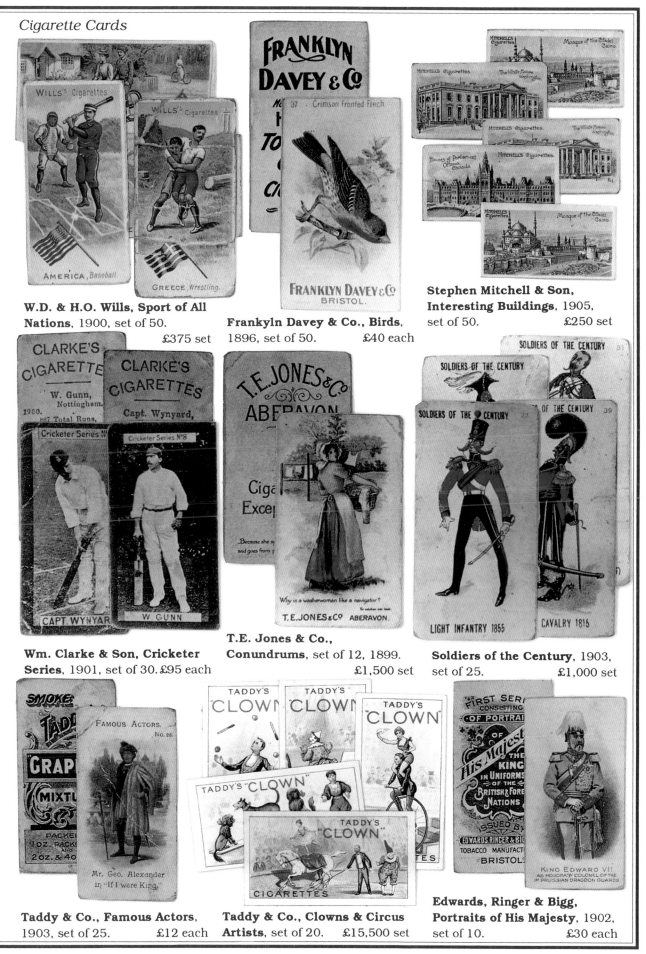

W.D. & H.O. Wills, Sport of All Nations, 1900, set of 50.
£375 set

Frankyln Davey & Co., Birds, 1896, set of 50.
£40 each

Stephen Mitchell & Son, Interesting Buildings, 1905, set of 50.
£250 set

Wm. Clarke & Son, Cricketer Series, 1901, set of 30. £95 each

T.E. Jones & Co., Conundrums, set of 12, 1899.
£1,500 set

Soldiers of the Century, 1903, set of 25.
£1,000 set

Taddy & Co., Famous Actors, 1903, set of 25.
£12 each

Taddy & Co., Clowns & Circus Artists, set of 20.
£15,500 set

Edwards, Ringer & Bigg, Portraits of His Majesty, 1902, set of 10.
£30 each

Cigarette Packets

Cigarettes began being sold in Britain in 1851. Initially they were sold in wrappers, but soon after, the cigarette packet was developed and since trade marks were first registered in 1876 over 30,000 different brands have appeared.

The hull and side packet came into use around 1890, and the flip-top, though it was invented in the USA in 1927, was not introduced into Britain until 1956, when it was first used for Churchman's No. 1.

Hair Pin Cigarettes, Virginia Tobacco, packet of 10, 1900–1920. £17

Rich Uncle Cigarettes by **S.J. Gore & Co., Old Kent Road, London**, packet of 5, 1900–1920. £20

Motor Cigarettes, packet of 10, 1940–1960. £4

Life Guard Cigarettes with patent cork holders by **Wm. Clarke & Sons, Liverpool & London**, packet of 5, 1900–1920. £20

The New Alliance best Virginia Cigarettes made by **David Corre & Co. London**, packet of 5, 1900–1920. £16

Grenadier Cigarettes by **W. & F. Faulkner, London**, packet of 5, 1920–1940. £8

Unicorn Virginia Coloured Cigarettes, gold tipped, packet of 10, manufactured in England by **Rothmans Ltd.**, 1940–1960. £5

Star of the World Cigarettes by the **J.L.S. Tobacco Co.**, packet of 5, 1900–1920. £18

Circus Girl Cigarettes by **Cohen, Weenen & Co., London**, packet of 5, 1900–1920. £20

(Hilary Humphries)

Cigarette Packets

Band Master Cigarettes, manufactured by **Cohen, Weenen & Co., London**, packet of 5, 1900–1920. £18

Dandy Dan Cigarettes by **A.H. Franks & Sons**, packet of 5, 1900–1920. £20

Raspberry Buds Cigarettes, packet of 7, by **Salmon & Gluckstein Ltd., London**, 1900–1920. £16

At Ease Cigarettes manufactured by **Cope, Bros. & Co., Ltd. Liverpool & London**, packet of 10, 1900–1920. £20

Bobs Cigarettes by **Symonds & Co., Pentonville Road, King's Cross**, packet of 5, 1900–1920. £20

Black & White Virginia Cigarettes, packet of 20, by **Marcovitch & Company, 84 Piccadilly, London**, 1940–1960. £2

The Chester Cup Cigarettes by **W.T. Davies & Sons, Chester**, packet of 20, 1900–1920. £15

Jolly Briton hand made cigarettes by **T.P. & R. Goodbody**, packet of 5, 1900–1920. £18

(Hilary Humphries)

Cigarette Packets

Island Queen Virginia Cigarettes, packet of 20, manufactured by **Murray Sons & Co. Ltd., London & Belfast**, 1940–1960. £5

Teddy Bear Virginia Cigarettes, packet of 10, by **Thomas Bear & Sons**, 1940–1960. £7

Cina Cigarettes, packet of 10, 1940–1960. £4

London Idol Virginia Cigarettes by **R. & J. Hill Ltd.**, complete with contents. £50

Adkin's Soldiers of the Queen Cigarettes by **Mardons Ltd., Bristol & London**, packet of 5, 1900–1920. £16

Elephant Cigarettes, packet of 10, by **Thomas Bear & Sons**, 1940–1960. £4

Cambridge Union Society Straight Cut Virginia Cigarettes, packet of 10, 1920–1940. £6

Navy Cut Cigarettes, packet of 20, by **A.I. Jones & Co. Ltd.**, 1920–1940. £9

Red Cats Virginia Cigarettes, packet of 10, 1940–1960. £3

The Don Cigarettes by **J.J. Holland**, packet of 5, 1900–1920. £15

Man of War Cigarettes manufactured by **Cope, Bros. & Co. Ltd., Liverpool & London**, packet of 10, 1900–1920. £18

(Hilary Humphries)

Cigarette Packets

Fusilier Cigarettes, The Marvel of the Age, manufactured by **J. & E. Woolf**, packet of 5, 1900–1920. £15

Ocean Prince Cigarettes made from Pure Virginia Tobacco by True British Labour, manufactured by **Adkin & Sons, London**, packet of 5, 1900–1920. £15

Freebooter Virginia Cigarettes, packet of 20, by **F. & J. Smith, Glasgow**, 1920–1940. £10

Clown Virginia Cigarettes, packet of 10, 1920–1940. £10

Bar One Cigarettes, packet of 20, 1940–1960. £2

Lifeguard Cigarettes, Balaclava, by **Wm. Clarke & Son**, complete with contents. £50

Turkish Blend Cigarettes, packet of 20, by **B. Morris & Sons Ltd., London**, 1940–1960. £4

Page Boy Cigarettes, packet of 10, 1940–1960. £3

Kits Cigarettes, packet of 20, by **W. Williams & Co., Chester**, 1920–1940. £10

(Hilary Humphries)

Cigarette Packets

Early 20th century **Guinea Gold Cigarettes** by G. Phillips & Sons complete with contents.
£50

Biggs Own Cigarettes, Cool & Fragrant, packet of 20, 1920–1940. £7

Park Lane Virginia Cigarettes, packet of 20, 1940–1960. £2

Pear Blossom Compressed Cigarettes, packet of 5, maufactured by A. Baker & Co. Ltd., 65 Holloway Road, London, 1900–1920. £18

Champion Cigarettes manufactured by **Cope, Bros. & Co. Ltd., Liverpool & London**, packet of 5, 1900–1910. £18

Pirate Cigarettes, packet of 20, by W.D. & H.O. Wills, Bristol & London, 1940–1960. £3

Miss Blanche Gold Leaf Virginia Cigarettes, packet of 10, 1940–1960. £3

All Gay Cigarettes by Harris's Factories, London, with handsome coloured photo, packet of 5, 1900–1920. £20

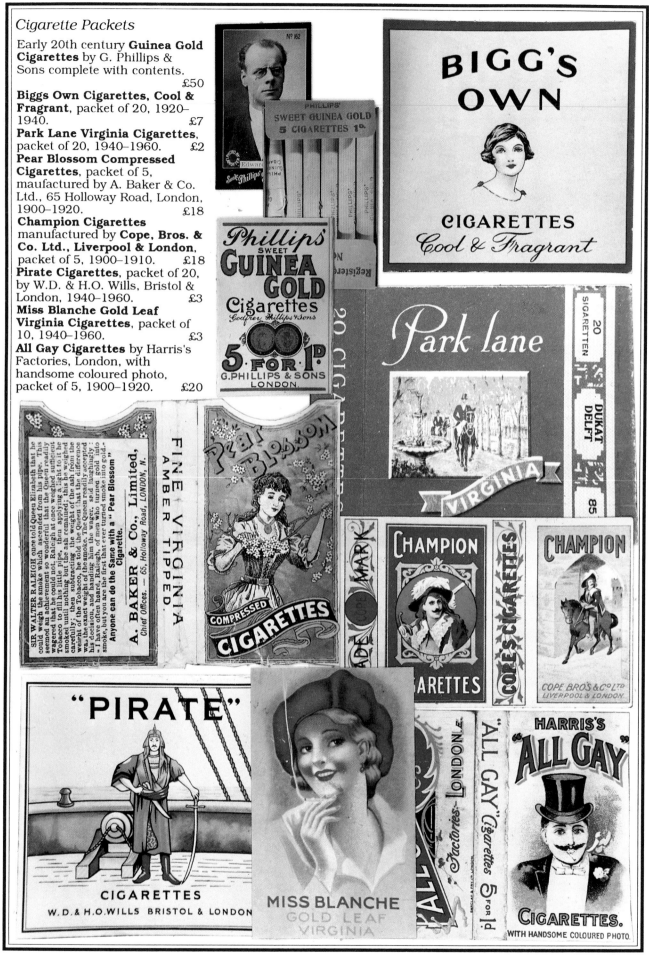

(Hilary Humphries)

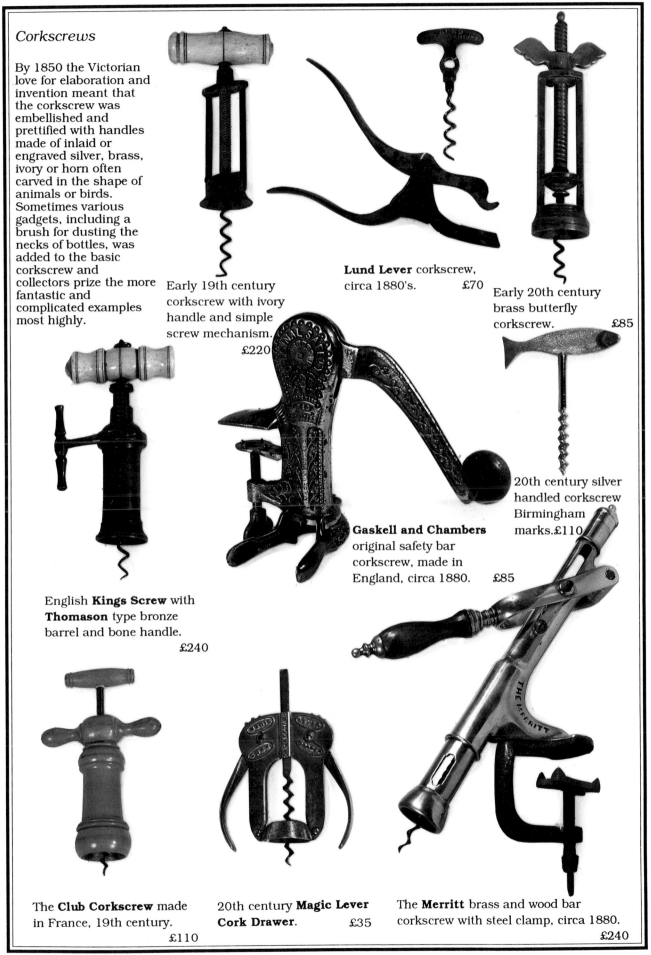

Corkscrews

By 1850 the Victorian love for elaboration and invention meant that the corkscrew was embellished and prettified with handles made of inlaid or engraved silver, brass, ivory or horn often carved in the shape of animals or birds. Sometimes various gadgets, including a brush for dusting the necks of bottles, was added to the basic corkscrew and collectors prize the more fantastic and complicated examples most highly.

Early 19th century corkscrew with ivory handle and simple screw mechanism. £220

Lund Lever corkscrew, circa 1880's. £70

Early 20th century brass butterfly corkscrew. £85

English **Kings Screw** with **Thomason** type bronze barrel and bone handle. £240

Gaskell and Chambers original safety bar corkscrew, made in England, circa 1880. £85

20th century silver handled corkscrew Birmingham marks. £110

The **Club Corkscrew** made in France, 19th century. £110

20th century **Magic Lever Cork Drawer**. £35

The **Merritt** brass and wood bar corkscrew with steel clamp, circa 1880. £240

(George Court)

Cricketing Memorabilia

Players Guest Cricket Final tickets 1987, signed by both teams. £50 each

England v Australia, Lords 1934, team signatures. £150

W.G. Grace, signed photograph. £250

Texaco One Day Cricket International Series, England v West Indies 1984, glass paperweight. £20

(T. Vennett Smith)

Cricketing Memorabilia

The Lords Taverners Trophy, presented for the Britannic Assurance Championships. £180

Lords Cricket Ground hat signed by the Nottinghamshire team. £60

Benson & Hedges Test Series Trophy, Australia v England 1982–3, to Derek Randall. £200

John Player & Sons, cigarette cards of Cricketers, 1938. £10

The Australian Cricketing Team 1888 by the **London Stereoscopic & Photographic Company Ltd**. £200

Signed miniature, **M.C.C. South African Team** 1938–1939. £20

(T. Vennett Smith)

Cricketing Memorabilia

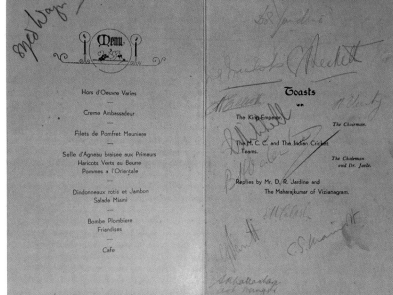

Prudential Trophy,
England v India, 1982.   £160

M.C.C. and Indian Cricket Team, signed menu, March 6th, 1934.   £100

Tamil Nadu Cricket Association Trophy,
Madras, 14.1.1977.   £30

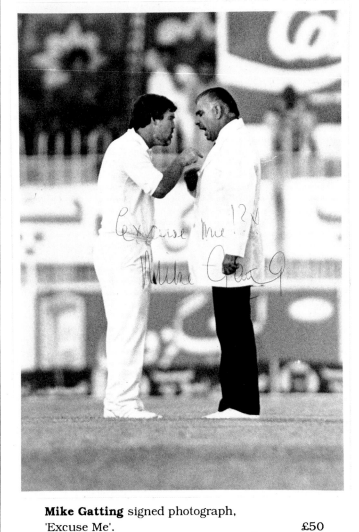

Mike Gatting signed photograph, 'Excuse Me'.   £50

England v Australia scorecard for 1882.   £120

(T. Vennett Smith)

Cricketing Memorabilia

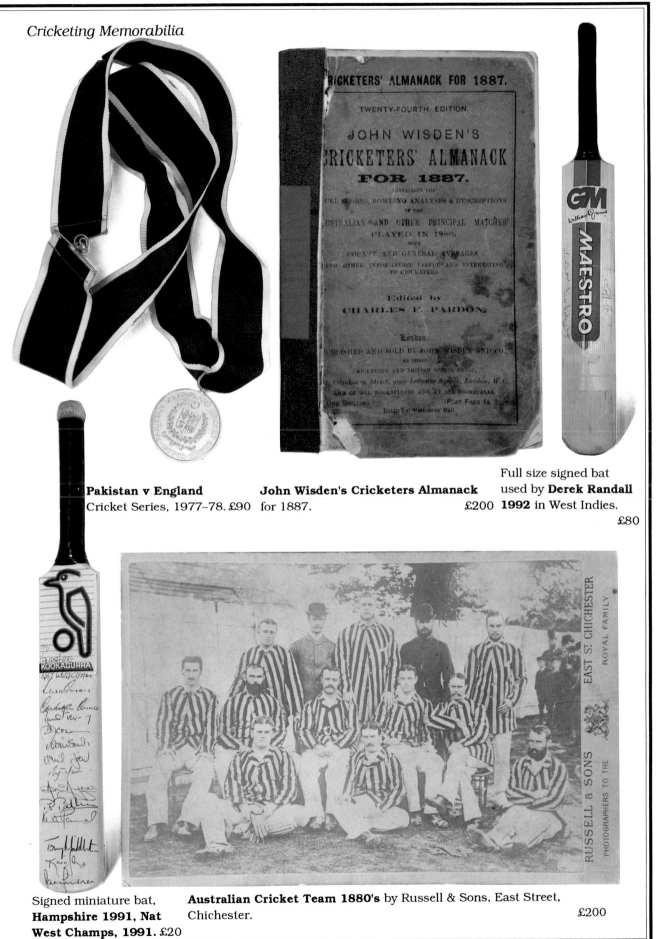

Pakistan v England
Cricket Series, 1977–78. £90

John Wisden's Cricketers Almanack
for 1887.
£200

Full size signed bat
used by **Derek Randall
1992** in West Indies.
£80

Signed miniature bat,
**Hampshire 1991, Nat
West Champs, 1991.** £20

Australian Cricket Team 1880's by Russell & Sons, East Street,
Chichester.
£200

(T. Vennett Smith)

Cricketing Memorabilia

Australia Day Olympic Sports Carnival, 1980. £40

A DINNER-DANCE

given to the

M. C. C.

AND

INDIAN CRICKET TEAMS

by

"THE TIMES OF INDIA"

IN AID OF

H. E. THE VICEROY'S EARTHQUAKE FUND

TAJ MAHAL HOTEL, BOMBAY

March 6th, 1934

M.C.C. and Indian Cricket Team, signed menu, March 6th 1934. £100

Dark blue sun hat signed by **Chris Lewis**. £60

Man of the Match Nat West Trophy, Nottinghamshire v Devon 1988, D.W. Randall. £180

Benson & Hedges Cup, Nottinghamshire v Somerset 1982, Final at Lords. £180

Full size signed bat, 1991, £90

Wilkinson Sword and Sun Award, Fielder of the Year 1979.£150

The Lords Taverners Trophy, presented for the **Schweppes** Championship. £180

(T. Vennett Smith)

Dolls

A **Kammer & Reinhardt** bisque character doll, German, circa 1909, 19in. high. (Sotheby's) £1,980

A **Tête Jumeau** moulded bisque doll, French, 1895, £3,300

A **François Gaultier** pressed bisque doll, French, circa 1880, (Sotheby's) £4,400

A **Henri Alexandre Bébé Phénix** pressed bisque doll, French, 1889, 15³/₄in. high. (Sotheby's) £2,200

A bisque headed bébé, 14in. high, stamped in red **Depose Tête Jumeau Bte**. (Christie's) £2,640

An **A. Thuillier** pressed bisque doll, French, circa 1875, 13¹/₂in. high. (Sotheby's) £14,300

Dolls

A bisque headed bébé with fixed blue eyes, impressed **Bru Jne 6**, 19in. high.
(Christie's) £15,400

Early 19th century split head doll with kid body, 24in. high.
(Lyle) £300

A **Kammer & Reinhardt** bisque doll with blonde hair and original clothes.
(Greenslades) £200

Late 19th century German doll by **Simon & Halbig**. (Lyle) £400

A good 'A' series **Jules Steiner Bébé**, 11in. (Bonhams) £1,700

A fine bébé impressed **Bru Jne 7**, circa 1880. (Christie's) £12,100

Dolls

A composition **Red Riding Hood** doll with sleeping eyes. (Greenslades) £190

Late 1970's American limited edition **'glamour'** doll, 28in. high complete with sequined top and roller skates. (Lyle) £200

Late 19th century German doll by **Armand Marseille** with original clothes and hair, 21in. high. (Lyle) £325

A fine **J.D. Kestner** bisque head **'googly'** eyed character doll, 16in. high. (Bonhams) £3,800

A rare carved and painted **Charles II** wooden doll with pink rouged cheeks, 13in. high, circa 1680. (Christie's) £71,500

A bisque headed bébé with blue lever operated sleeping eyes by **Steiner**. (Christie's) £2,860

Domestic Instruments

A very rare American **Morris**
typewriter dating from 1885 of
which only four are known.
(Auction Team Köln)   £13,500

Norwegian wall telephone
with decorative cast iron
back plate by
**Aktieselskabet Elektrisk
Bureau Kristiania, Oslo**,
circa 1890.
(Auction Team Köln) £1,100

Late 19th century walnut cased stereoscopic
viewer by **Murray & Heath**.
(Lyle)   £275

Florence cast iron sewing machine with gilt decoration,
circa 1875. (George Court)   £250

1930's metal framed fan by **Frost**,
16in. high. (Paul Spindley)   £40

Domestic Instruments

Monopol, early German spoke wheel calculating machine, 1894.
(Auction Team Köln)   £3,500

The first ever hot air fan, 113cm. high, circa 1860.
(Auction Team Köln)   £2,185

An English **Stanley** hand telephone, circa 1880.
(Auction Team Köln)
£370

An unusual 19th century **Davenport** cased sewing machine by J. Davies & Co. (Phillips) £1,300

The **Eclipse**, an example of the first known electric toaster, made in England, 1893.
(Auction Team Köln)   £1,310

Domestic Instruments

A **Wimhurst** pattern electrostatic plate machine with six segmented glass contra-rotating plates, 27in. wide. (Christie's) £3,080

Arithometer, the first mass produced calculating machine by **Thomas De Colmar**, circa 1850. (Auction Team Köln) £2,670

The **Brunette**, a 35mm hand cranked cinematographic projector in stylised metal case. (Christie's S. Ken.) £462

Doulton Figures

The first highly skilled figure maker who worked for Doulton was George Tinworth, the Lambeth sculptor, but his figure output was small.

However in 1889 Charles J. Noke left the Royal Worcester Company where he was already showing his prodigious talent as a sculptor and went to work for Doulton's at Burslem. The son of an antique dealer who appreciated the fine vases and figures made by Derby, Bow, Chelsea, Meissen and Sevres, he was fired with the ambition of recreating the once greatly admired Staffordshire figure making industry.

Around 1912 he introduced a figure range which was released to the public in 1913 after Queen Mary, on a visit to Burslem, exclaimed "What a Darling!" at the sight of a figure called 'Bedtime' modelled by Charles Vyse.

'Bedtime' was re-christened 'Darling' and proved to be one of the most popular Doulton figures ever produced. It is still in production.

Hinged Parasol, HN1578. £250

Promenade, HN2076. £800

Rhythm, HN1903. £300

Pamela, HN1469. £250

Fruit Gathering, HN707. £750

Pantalettes, HN1362. £180

Miss Demure, HN1402. £95

Sunshine Girl, HN1344. £850

Doulton Figures

Omar Khayyam, HN2247. £90

Autumn Breezes, HN1913. £95

Spring Flowers, HN1807. £170

Belle O'The Ball, HN1997. £110

Pied Piper, HN1215. £400

Monte Carlo, HN2332. £180   **Rustic Swain**, HN1745. £750   **Folly**, HN1335. £600

Doulton Figures

Tête-à-Tête, HN799.
£600

Ladybird, HN1638. £450

Grandma, HN2052. £135

Stop Press, HN2683. £75

Swimmer, HN1270. £600

Charlie Chapman, HN2771. £100

Abdullah, HN1410. £420

Wandering Minstrel, HN1224. £800

Doulton Figures

Bonnie Lassie, HN1626. £120

Vivienne, HN2073. £135

Detective, HN2359. £68

Tildy, HN1859. £200

Clown, HN2890. £90

Boatman, HN2417. £75

Chloe, HN1479. £130   **Daffy-Down-Dilly**, HN1712. £130

Clock Maker, HN2279. £120

70

Doulton Figures

Boy with Turban, HN1210. £275

Coppelia, HN2115. £275

Milkmaid, HN2057. £70

Gandalf, HN2911. £38

Make Believe, HN2225. £35

Polly Peachum, HN550. £160

Perfect Pair, HN581. £450

Prized Possessions, HN2942. £160

Ermine Coat, HN1981. £110

Irish Colleen, HN766. £650

Games

Before the age of television, family evening entertainment used often to consist of a board game or card game such as Happy Families, and the nostalgia element plays a large part in the enthusiastic collecting of games today. Favourites included Ludo, and Snakes and Ladders, and many offered education as well as amusement in the form of word games or general knowledge tests.

Aviation, The Aerial Tactics game of **Attack and Defence** by **H.P. Gibson & Sons**, early 1950's. (George Court) £45

Meteor by **Fad Richter & Cie**, circa 1920. (Street Jewellery) £15

Emergency Ward 10 game produced by **Bell**, 14in. x 14in., 1958. (Sam Weller) £8

Showgirl Models playing cards, 1970's. (Yesterday's Paper) £4

Games

Magic Robot game by **Merit**, 15^1/$_2$in. x 10in., 1960's. (Sam Weller) £8

Jackpot supplied by **Pryor Bros., Orpington**, 5^1/$_4$in. high. (Sam Weller) £4

Biba Pin Ups playing cards, 1970's. (Yesterday's Paper) £15

Board game **'Sorry'** with cards and game pieces, circa 1910. (Sam Weller) £15

Picture Printing & Letter Type Outfit No. 125, by **John Bull**, 12^1/$_2$in. x 10^1/$_2$in. (Sam Weller) £15

John Bull Printing Outfit No. 18, by **Carbak**, 9in. x 6^1/$_2$in. (Sam Weller) £4

Games

Horseracing game.
(Street Jewellery)   £15

Find the Car by **C.W. Faulkner**, 1920's.
(Yesterday's Paper)   £6

Vargas Glamour playing cards, circa 1950.   £50

Railroad Switch game, 16in. x 11in.
(Sam Weller)   £5

Games

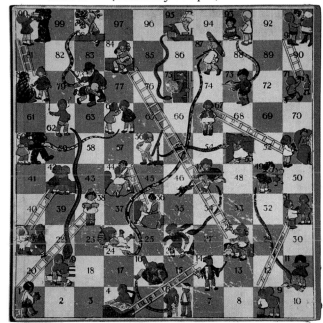

Wireless Whist by **The Dainty Series**,
1920's.   (Yesterday's Paper)   £6

Air Raiding game by **Chad Valley Toys**, 1950's.   £15

Snakes & Ladders game.
(Street Jewellery)   £15

Sport-a-Crest, Dennis's Dainty Series.
(Yesterday's Paper)   £6

Tops and Tails card game, 1960's.
(Yesterday's Paper)   £4

Mid 1960's, **'Monte Carlo'** game, 15in.
high.   (Sam Weller)   £12

Goss Cottages

The famous Goss factory which started producing china in 1858 started a very popular line in attractive little cottages modelled on the homes of famous people in 1893 and continued making them till 1929. Among the 51 different types they sold were copies of Anne Hathaway's cottage at Stratford on Avon and Robert Burns' home at Alloway. The cottages were often pastille burners and they sold well because they made attractive and cheap souvenirs. Today they are among the most desirable items in the vast Goss range for collectors who specialise in the products of that enterprising company. The cottages are usually marked with the name W.H. Goss and a goshawk with wings outstretched.

Manx Cottage nightlight, Isle of Man, 122mm. long. £160

Miss Ellen Terry's Farm near Tenterden in Kent, 70mm. long. £310

St. Catherine's Chapel, Abbotsbury, 87mm. long. £420

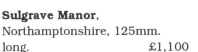

Old Market House at Ledbury, 68mm. long. £290

John Knox's House at Edinburgh, 102mm. high. £375

Sulgrave Manor, Northamptonshire, 125mm. long. £1,100

Dr. Samuel Johnson's House, Lichfield, 75mm. high. £150

Christchurch, **Old Court House**, 76mm. £325

Shakespeare's Cottage, Stratford-on-Avon, 65mm. long. £75

Priest's House, Prestbury, 90mm. long. £1,050

(The Goss & Crested China Co.)

Goss Cottages

St. Nicholas Chapel, Lantern Hill, Ilfracombe, 74mm. high.
£160

Issac Walton's Birthplace, Shallowford, 86mm. long. £350

Charles Dickens House at Gads Hill, near Rochester. £130

Old Maids Cottage, Lee, Devon, 73mm. long. £120

Southampton Tudor House, 83mm. long. £285

The Old Thatched Cottage, Poole, 68mm. long. £400

Thomas Hardy's Birthplace, Dorchester, 100mm. long. £350

The Goss Oven, Orange chimney version, 75mm. long. £215

First and Last House in England, with annexe, 140mm. long. £750

The Feathers Hotel, Ledbury, 114mm. long. £800

Look-out House at Newquay, 65mm. high. £95

Ann Hathaway's Cottage, Shottery, at Stratford-on-Avon. 148mm. long. £265

(The Goss & Crested China Co.)

Greetings Cards

Victorian popularisation of Christmas started a vogue for Christmas cards. Over the years many famous artists have designed greeting cards and if the artist can be identified, the card's value in enhanced. Among the more accessible cards for collectors are deckle edged cards dating from between 1918 and 1945 and photographically reproduced cards with hand coloured pictures. Many attractive examples were produced in the Beagle and Rotary series.

Greetings from Nigeria. £2

'Christmas Greetings and All Good Wishes' £5

'All Best Wishes', late Victorian lithographic card. £15

'Ever Free', woven silk Christmas card, circa 1915. £10

'To Greet you at Christmas.' £3

'Bright and Glad be your season'. £8

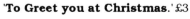

'Christmas Bells', 'A Merry Christmas to You'. £5

Greetings Cards

From One of the Canadian Field Artillery.

Teddy Bear Christmas Card, **'With every good wish**', circa 1910.   £12

May you be after all the sweet things like Raspberry Jam this season.   £4

'A Gude New Year and Mony o' Them'.   £3

Late Victorian card **'Wishes'**. £15

'A Happy Christmas'.   £7

'May Your New Year be bright and happy.'   £3

'Merry Christmas'.   £10

Greetings Cards

Christmas card sent by **Sir Henry Cole** to **William Makepeace Thackeray**. £2,500

Moping is Folly U.O.2.B. Jolly, late Victorian card. £12

'A Birthday Greeting, O may no cloud o'ershadow thee, And thou from every ill be free', late Victorian card. £6

All happiness be thine, this Christmastide. £8

All good wishes. £4

Much Fun and Merriment, Victorian card. £10

Merry Christmas to You, printed in Bavaria. £8

The Castle of Mey, from **Queen Elizabeth the Queen Mother.** £70

If this card against the light you scan, it will reveal the lamps of Japan, Victorian card. £10

A Happy New Year, late Victorian card. £6

Christmas 1890 from **Mr & Mrs R.J. Stamp.** £5

Hollywood Posters

The first posters were made by wood or copper engraving, a process which was both costly and complicated. With stone lithography, a process using limestone slabs as printing plates, came radical changes. An artist would create his handpainted design in fine detail and it would then be reproduced on the slab, resulting in a poster which was both beautiful and distinctive in appearance. With the advent of sound, poster quality deteriorated, perhaps because of rising film production costs.

It is thought that, for the average picture, between 7,000 and 12,000 posters were created and distributed among cinema owners, who had to return them after the film run against credit on future posters. For a 'blockbuster' the studio might print twice or even four times as many, but as those returned posters were recycled to as many other cinemas as their condition allowed, the wear and tear of repeated use meant that very few have survived, and even fewer in good condition.

The Pilgrim, First National, 1923, six-sheet, linen backed, 81 x 81in. £6,705

Rebel without a Cause, Warner Brothers, 1955, six-sheet, linen backed, 81 x 81in. £2,420

The War of the Worlds, Paramount, 1953, six-sheet, linen backed, 81 x 81in. £2,904

Blonde Venus, Paramount, 1933, original Belgian poster, linen backed, 30 x 24in. £5,748

(Christie's East)

Hollywood Posters

The Big Parade, MGM, 1927, one-sheet, linen backed, 41 x 27in. £1,516

Forbidden, Columbia, 1932, one-sheet, linen backed, 41 x 27in. £991

Tanned Legs, RKO, 1929, one-sheet, linen backed, 41 x 27in. £1,210

A Dog's Life, First National, 1918, one-sheet, linen backed, 41 x 27in. £9,328

Son of Frankenstein, 1939, one sheet, linen backed, 41in. x 27in. £7,865

Steamboat round the Bend, Fox, 1935, one-sheet, linen backed, 41 x 27in. £605

East is West, First National, 1922, one-sheet, linen backed, 41 x 27in. £484

The Bellhop, Vitagraph, 1921, one-sheet, linen backed, 41 x 27in. £393

The Mummy, Universal, 1932, Title lobby card, 11 x 14in. £5,748

She Done Him Wrong, Paramount, 1933, six-sheet, linen backed, 81 x 81in. £3,032

Way Out West, MGM, 1937, half-sheet, unfolded, 22 x 28in. £1,691

(Christie's East)

Hollywood Posters

A Dog's Life, First National, 1918, six-sheet, linen backed, 81 x 81in. £19, 360

The Wizard of Oz, MGM, 1939, three-sheet, linen backed, 81 x 41in. £13,915

King Kong, RKO, 1933, three-sheet, linen backed, 81 x 41in. £31,460

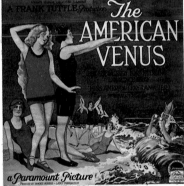

The American Venus, Paramount, 1926, six-sheet, linen backed, 81 x 81in. £1,982

Atom Man vs. Superman, Columbia, 1950, 81 x 81in. £4,538

The Old Dark House, Universal, 1932, one-sheet, 41 x 27in. £26,620

(Christie's East)

Hollywood Posters

The Rough Diamond, Fox, 1921, one-sheet, linen backed, 41 x 27in. £641

The Wolf Man, Universal, 1941, one-sheet, 41 x 27in. £9,680

Under the Yoke, Fox, 1918, one-sheet, linen backed, 41 x 27in. £454

The Bait, Paramount, 1921, one-sheet, linen backed, 41 x 27in. £554

Manhattan Melodrama, MGM, 1934, half-sheet, unfolded, 22 x 28in. £1,691

Citizen Kane, RKO, 1941, half-sheet, unfolded, 22 x 28in. £2,041

The Cabinet of Dr. Caligari, film poster, **Goldwyn**, 1921, one-sheet, linen backed, 41in. x 27in.
In 1919, Robert Wiene directed a film in Germany that changed the face of the cinema. The Cabinet of Dr. Caligari is told from the perspective of its lead character, revealed in the final reel to be a madman. In 1921, a daring Sam Goldwyn brought the film to the United States. £19,822

American Entertainment Co., ca. 1900, one sheet, linen backed, 28 x 41in. £1,982

(Christie's East)

Hollywood Posters

**What Do Men Want?,
Lois Weber Productions**,
1921, one-sheet, linen
backed, 41 x 27in.   £3,032

Citizen Kane, RKO,
1941, one-sheet, linen
backed, 41 x 27in.
£12,100

**The Devil is a Woman,
Paramount**, 1935, one-
sheet, linen backed,
41 x 27in.   £9,075

**The Wild Party,
Paramount**, 1929,
one-sheet, linen backed,
41 x 27in.   £1,574

**Out West, Paramount-
Arbuckle**, 1918, one-sheet,
linen backed, 41 x 27in.
£2,904

The Son of the Sheik, United Artists,
1926, half-sheet, unfolded, 22 x 28in.
£1,458

**Society Dog Show,
Disney**, 1939, one-
sheet, linen backed,
41 x 27in.   £5,748

**40,000 Miles with
Lindbergh, MGM**, 1928,
one-sheet, linen backed,
41 x 27in.   £3,025

**The Siren Call,
Paramount**, 1921, one-
sheet, linen backed,
41 x 27in.   £525

**The Master Mystery,
Octagon Films**, 1919,
one-sheet, linen backed,
41 x 27in.   £9,075

**The Toll Gate, Paramount
Artcraft**, 1920, one-sheet,
linen backed, 41 x 27in.
£1,399

(Christie's East)

Hollywood Posters

Know Your Men, Fox, 1921, one-sheet, linen backed, 41 x 27in. £875

Charlie Chan's Chance, Fox, 1931, one-sheet, linen backed, 41 x 27in. £1,166

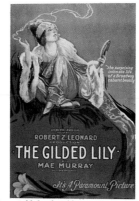

The Gilded Lily, Paramount, 1921, one-sheet, linen backed, 41 x 27in. £933

East is West, First National, 1922, one-sheet, linen backed, 41 x 27in. £1,982

Captain January, 20th Century Fox, 1936, one-sheet, linen backed, 41 x 27in. £1,210

The Birth of a Nation, Epoch Producing Corp., 1915, one-sheet, linen backed, 41 x 27in. £15,730

Behind the Mask, Columbia, 1932, one-sheet, linen backed, 41 x 27in. £424

Horse Feathers, Paramount, 1932, one-sheet, linen backed, 41 x 27in. £2,904

The Wizard of Oz, MGM, 1939, half-sheet, unfolded, 22 x 28in. £5,830

The Woman Alone, Gaumont British, 1936, one-sheet, linen backed, 41 x 27in. £1,166

(Christie's East)

Jigsaw Puzzles

A London map maker invented the first jigsaw puzzle in the 1760's by mounting a map on a sheet of mahogany and cutting it into small pieces with a fine marquetry saw. The reassembling of it was intended to help pupils learn geography. He sold his 'dissecting maps' in wooden boxes with sliding lids and his idea was copied by other manufacturers.

At the end of the 19th century, coloured labels showing the finished puzzle were pasted on box lids and they were worth collecting on their own. Mass production techniques and the use of plywood and fret saws meant that it was possible to turn out large numbers of puzzles at a fairly low cost and jigsaws became a craze in the 1920's and 30's before the advent of television. Some of the most famous firms who produced them were Raphael Tuck who made the Zag Zaw and Chad Valley who produced jigsaws for Great Eastern Railway.

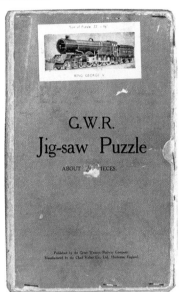

'Henley Bridge', 4th Series standard size puzzle of 200 pieces, $9^1/_4$in. x $6^1/_2$in., opening tab book box.
(R. Bannister) £25

'King George V', G.W.R. 200 piece jigsaw, manufactured by **Chad Valley Co. Ltd.**, 1933.
(R. Bannister) £45

Valentines & Sons Dundee, 'On Board an Aircraft Carrier', 1950's.
(R. Bannister) £20

The Piglets (Beatles Spoof) jigsaw, circa 1964.
(Yesterday's Paper) £10

'Windsor Castle', 1st series, **G.W.R.** jigsaw of 150 pieces made by **Chad Valley**.
(R. Bannister) £20

'Oxford' two tone sepia puzzle of 150 pieces published by **The Great Western Railway Company**, $10^3/_4$in. x $6^3/_4$in., 1924.
(R. Bannister) £30

Jigsaw Puzzles

'Vikings Landing at St. Ives', Series 3,
375 pieces, 12¹/₂in. x 7¹/₂in., 1930's.
(R. Bannister)   £30

The Cornish Riviera Express, Series 1,
jigsaw of 150 pieces, 10in. x 6in., 1924.
(R. Bannister)   £25

Playboy Playmate puzzle.
(Yesterday's Paper)   £12

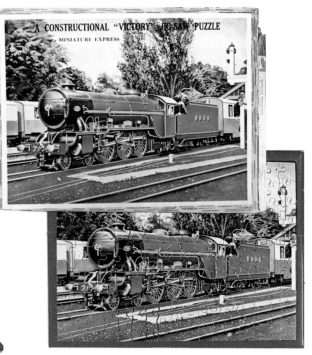

A constructional **'Victory'** jigsaw puzzle
depicting a Miniature Express with train
raised in relief, made by **G.J. Hayter &
Co., Boscombe.**
(Sheffield Railwayana Auctions)   £25

Giles jigsaw puzzle, 1976.
(Yesterday's Paper)   £5

'Hunting Scene' by **J.S. Sanderson,
Wells**, 200 pieces, 14in. x 10in.
(R. Bannister)   £20

Jigsaw Puzzles

Travel Association 'Come to Britain' interlocking jigsaw puzzle by **Chad Valley**, 500 pieces. (R. Bannister)   £50

'Drake Goes West', 4th series, large size jigsaw, 400 pieces, book type box, 1934. (R. Bannister)   £35

'Brazenose College, Oxford' series 2 jigsaw, 400 pieces, sleeve box, 1933. (R. Bannister)   £25

Steptoe & Son jigsaw puzzle, 240 pieces, 1964. (Lyle)   £6

'The Village Pond', Excelsior jigsaw puzzle by **Philmar**, 1200 pieces, 34in. x 23in. (Lyle)   £15

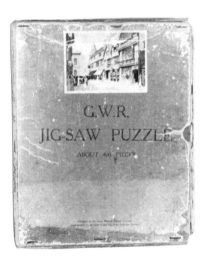

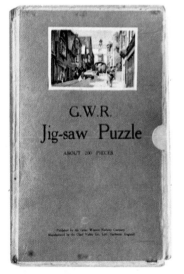

Cunard Series White Star Line jigsaw puzzle, **R.M.S. Queen Mary**, 200 pieces, made by **Chad Valley**. (R. Bannister)   £30

'Stratford Upon Avon' Harvard House, Series 2, jigsaw puzzle of 400 pieces, 1933. (R. Bannister)   £25

Historic Totnes, sleeve type box, Series 2 jigsaw, 200 pieces, 1933. (R. Bannister)   £35

Just William Books

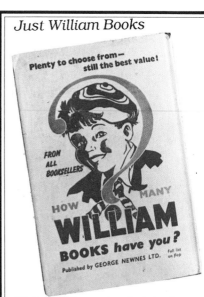

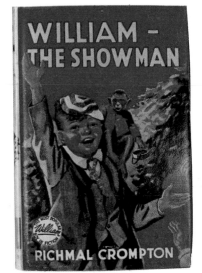

William the Showman, 12th edition, 1956. £12

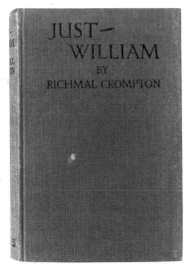

Just William, 1929 edition, without dust jacket. £8

Richmal Crompton (original name Lamburn) was born in 1890 in Bury, Lancashire. She was educated in Lancashire and Derbyshire and at the Royal Holloway College, where she graduated in Classics. She became a teacher, and published her first book about that engaging ruffian William in 1922, and the series has continued to delight generations of children ever since. Though she published some 50 adult titles, it is for her William books that she is remembered today. Surprisingly, first editions of later books can be worth more than the earlier titles. Most were illustrated by Thomas Henry, who, on his death, was succeeded by Henry Ford. Ford illustrated just three before Crompton's death on 11 January 1969. Her last book, published posthumously, was 'William the Lawless', and could be worth £300 in mint condition.

Just William's Luck, 1st edition, 1948, no dust jacket. £20

William the Pirate, 1st edition, 1958. £15

William the Bold, 2nd edition, 1952. £20

William the Outlaw, 23rd edition, 1953. £10

William the Fourth, 23rd edition, 1963. £6

(Paul Sheppard)

Just William Books

William the Rebel, 16th edition, 1954.   £12

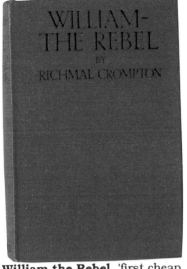

William the Rebel, 'first cheap edition', October 1933, no dust jacket.   £10

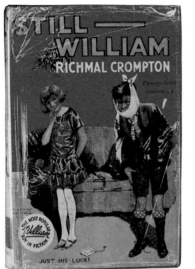

Still William, 26th edition, 1935.   £10

William Again, 27th edition, October 1941.   £10

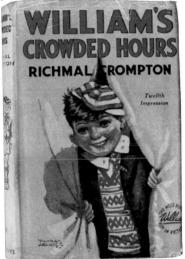

William's Crowded Hours, 12th edition, November 1941.   £12

William in Trouble, 23rd impression, 1951.   £10

William the Explorer, 1st edition. 1960.   £75

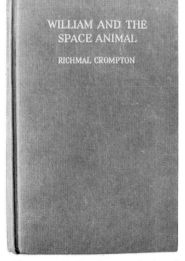

William and the Space Animal, 1st edition, without dust jacket. £30

William and the Space Animal, 1st edition, 1956.   £100

(Paul Sheppard)

Lamps

An important and rare **Tiffany Studios** leaded glass table lamp, 48in high.
(Phillips)   £60,000

Tiffany bronze and favrile glass ten light lily lamp, 22in. high.
(Skinner Inc.)   £15,000

Batwomen, a painted bronze and ivory figural table lamp by **Roland Paris**, 93cm. high.
(Phillips)   £7,200

Daum cameo glass table lamp, 26¹/₂in. high.(Skinner Inc.) £7,600

Early **Tiffany** bronze **Tyler** lamp, 24in. high.(Skinner Inc.) £25,000

1930's figural plaster lamp with contemporary shade. (Lyle) £100

Lantern Slides

The idea of illuminating an object from behind so as to cast a shadow on a wall or screen originated in the Far East, and caught on in Europe in the 17th century. From then on it was in constant development and by the nineteenth century magic lantern shows had become popular both as domestic and public entertainment.

The earliest slides were quite large and elaborately hand painted, and often came in mahogany frames.

Litho printed slide, '**Zeppelin**' airship.   £5

'**Ramsgate Harbour**', hand painted slide, 1870, by **Cox, 100 Newgate Street, London**. £25

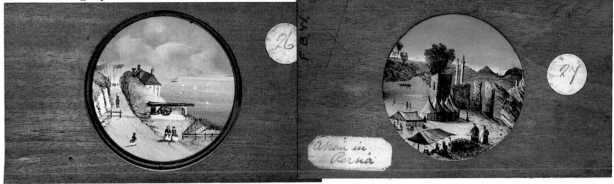

'**Queen Elizabeth Gun**', **Dover**, hand painted slide, 1870.   £25

'**Persian View**' hand painted slide, 1870.   £25

Queen Victoria at her Highland Home'.   £10

Litho printed slide, '**Bleriot**'.   £8

Litho printed slide '**Good Night**'.   £5

Arctic Regions' by **W.B. & D. Newton, Fleet Street, Temple Bar, London**, circa 1870.   £25

London Bridge, litho printed slide.   £5

(Dave Lewis)

Magazines

Left

Everybody's, Baron – Photographer issue, July 1956. £4

Picture Post, 'A Plan for Britain', Jan 1941 £5

Red Letter, For the Family Circle, October 1952. £2

Harrison's Young Ladies Journal, August 1914. £10

Souvenir of the Royal Jubilee, 1935. £8

English Illustrated Magazine with cover design by **Alphonse Mucha**, 1898. £20

Silver Star and Golden Star, March 30th 1950. £2

Famous Crimes Past and Present, Charles Peace. £6

Right

Parisiana, Les Bonnes Amies, Jan 1930. £8

London Life, Summer Special, 1933. £25

Woman, The National Weekly, Sept 1937. £8

Woman's Own No 1, February 27th 1937. £15

The Burr McIntosh Monthly, 1907 with illustrations by **Alphonse Mucha**. £20

London Calling, A Bright Paper for Bright People. £5

The Nudist, Sunshine & Health, 1939. £8

(Yesterday's Paper)

Magazines

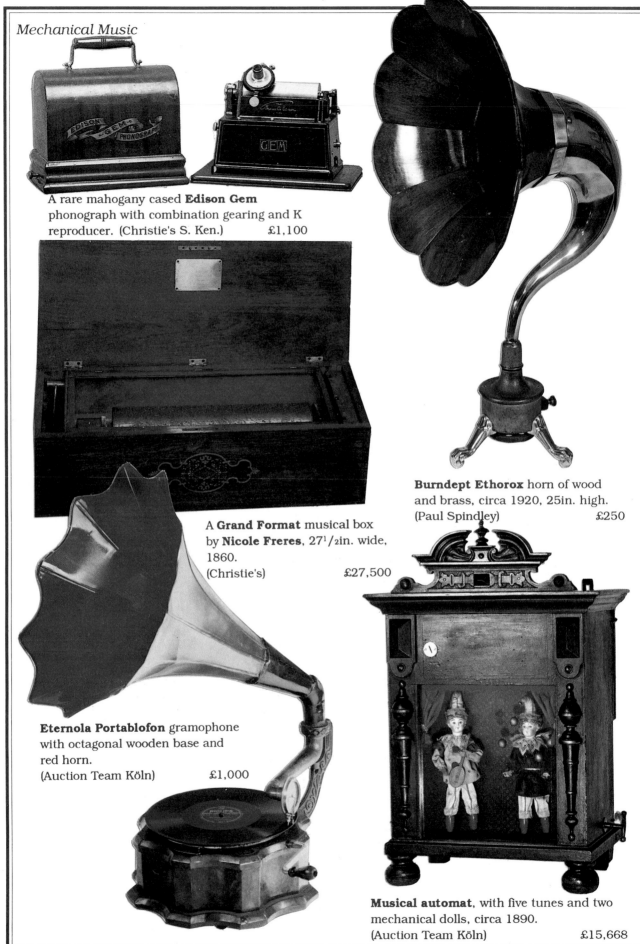

Mechanical Music

A rare mahogany cased **Edison Gem** phonograph with combination gearing and K reproducer. (Christie's S. Ken.) £1,100

A **Grand Format** musical box by **Nicole Freres**, 27¹/₂in. wide, 1860. (Christie's) £27,500

Burndept Ethorox horn of wood and brass, circa 1920, 25in. high. (Paul Spindley) £250

Eternola Portablofon gramophone with octagonal wooden base and red horn. (Auction Team Köln) £1,000

Musical automat, with five tunes and two mechanical dolls, circa 1890. (Auction Team Köln) £15,668

Mechanical Music

A hand turned **Tinfoil**
phonograph with brass mandrel
on steel threaded arbor, 15in.
wide.
(Christie's S. Ken.) £3,520

Edison Home phonograph,
Model A, the first **Edison**
cylinder player with the
banner emblem, 1898.
(Auction Team Köln) £825

A rare **Gramophone Company**
de luxe gramophone, 64in. high,
1920–22. (Christie's) £3,850

A German **Komet** penny in the
slot upright disc musical box,
circa 1900, 30in. wide.
(Bearne's) £5,800

A fine **Mikado** polyphon hall
clock, 104¹/₂in. high.
(Christie's) £23,100

Miniature Fireplaces

In the days when a fire was the heart of every home and advertising literature was not the glossy colourful thing it is today, long-suffering fireplace salesmen used to cart round with them miniature examples of their wares. These would be produced with meticulous attention to detail from the genuine materials from which their full-size counterparts would be made.

Scottish **cast iron fireplace** with **thistle decoration**, circa 1880. £120

Coloured **cast iron miniature fireplace** with the **Kendrick coat of arms**, 1880's. £160

19th century **pewter miniature grate**. £75

Cast iron **miniature fireplace** embellished with a Victorian coat of arms, circa 1880. £220

Late 1920's **tinplate moneybox** in the form of a fireplace by **John Wright & Co.** £85

(George Court)

Paperbacks

The publishing house Tauchnitz brought out paperbacks as long ago as 1837 but it was not for another hundred years that the idea was taken up in Britain in 1935 when the first Penguin books appeared.

Cora Pearl by **Bree Narran**, 1930's. £4

Boot Boys by **Richard Allen**, 1972. £3

The Monk by **M.G. Lewis**, 1960. £3

This Thing Called 'Sin' by **Roland Vane**, 1950. £12

The Turn of The Screw by **Henry James**, 1958. £2

The Story of My Heart by **Richard Jefferies**, Penguin Illustrated Classic, 1938. £5

Dig That Crazy Grave by **Richard S. Prather**, 1961. £3

The Velvet Underground by **Michael Leigh**, 1967. £5

Ariel, by **André Maurois**, **No. 1, Penguin**, 1935. £100

How to Pass Your Driving Test by **H. Sweet**, 1955, 7in. x 4¹/₂in. £2

The Auction of Souls, 1950. £8

The Peddler by **Richard S. Prather**, 1952. £4

The Hot Rod by **Nat Karta**, 1950's. £8

Typee by **Melville** with Wood Engravings by Robert Gibbings, Penguin Illustrated Classic, 1938. £5

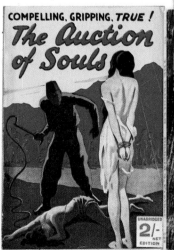

(Yesterday's Paper)

Paperbacks

The Mini Skirt and Beyond, 1970. £12

Floosie for Hire by Rex Richards, 1950. £8

Hell of a Dame by Hank Janson, 1960. £6

No Orchids for Miss Blandish by James Hadley Chase, 1955. £4

Avengers by John Garforth, 1967. £5

Suedehead by Richard Allen, 1981. £3

Strike for Death by John Creasey, 1960. £3

Marijuana Girl by N.R. De Mexico, 1969. £10

Confessions of a Kept Man by John O'Day, 1966. £6

City of Spades by Colin Macinnes, 1959. £4

Lose This Gun by Hank Janson, 1958. £4

You're Dead, My Lovely by Gene Ross, 1950. £12

(Yesterday's Paper)

Paperbacks

Trouble for Skinhead by Richard Allen, 1973. £3

The White Slaves of London by W.N. Willis, 1950's. £8

Inspector West at Home by John Creasey, 1965. £3

No Dice by Al Bocca, 1951. £5

Tomboy by Hal Ellson, 1952 £5

Sintime Beatniks by D.S. Froeman, 1967. £4

Earthlight by Arthur C Clarke, 1957. £3

A Walk on the Wild Side by Nelson Algren, 1960. £5

Gidget in Love by Frederick Kohner, 1965. £4

Sin Street by Paul Reville, 1950's. £12

Deadline by Patrick Macnee, 1965. £5

Stool-Pigeon Pie by Nick Rosso, 1950. £8

Petrol Pump Globes

Petrol Pumps were first used in America for about ten years before they came to Britain where the first pump was introduced by the A.A. Their pumps were topped with bright yellow globes to show they were associated with the organisation.

Cleveland Premium globe, 1950's. £250

BP Globe, 1930's. £120

Buffalo Gasoline globe, reproduction. £85

Jet plastic globe, 1960's. £40

Mobil globe, late 1950's, early 1960's. £150

Bulldog plastic globe, 1970's. £35

Russian Oil Products, 1930's. £200

Shell globe, 1950's. £200

Shell Diesoline globe, 1950's. £175

Regent globe, early 1960's. £150

Pink Paraffin globe. £75

BP Regular globe, late 1950's. £150

(The Period Petrol Pump Co.)

Petrol Pump Globes

Fina Super globe, 1930's. £350
Power globe, 1950's. £150
Fina globe, 1930's. £300
Esso Extra globe, 1950's £150
Super Shell (Blue) globe. £225
The Period Petrol Pump Co.
plastic globe, mid 1960's. £70
National Benzole globe, 1950's.
£95
Regent globe. £175
Regent TT globe. £90
BP Super globe, late 1950's.
£150
Not For Resale globe. £65
Super Shell globe. £225
Esso Mixture globe, 1950's.
£150

(The Period Petrol Pump Co.)

A Fortune in your Attic

Photographs

There are two schools of photography collecting. Firstly, specialists seek out photographs taken by the famous names of the art – William Henry Fox Talbot and Julia Margaret Cameron for example.

The other popular area is photographs of British towns and slum scenes or pictures of ordinary people working at their jobs, particularly agricultural labourers in the days before mechanisation.

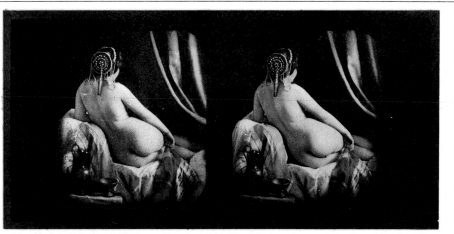

Reclining Nude, 1850's, stereoscopic **Daguerreotype**, hand painted, gilt highlight, paper taped.   (Christie's)   £8,800

Unpublished photograph of **Winston Churchill**. (T. Vennett Smith)   £70

Algerian Woman, early 1850's **Calotype** possibly by **Charles Marville**, $8^7/8$ x $7^1/8$in.   (Christie's)   £15,400

An albumen print of **Mrs. Herbert Duckworth**, 1867, by **Julia Margaret Cameron**, $13^1/2$in. x $9^3/4$in., mounted on grey card. (Christie's)   £14,300

Robert Howlett albumen print of **Isambard Kingdom Brunel and Launching Chains of the Great Eastern**, 1857. (Christie's)   £8,250

Pin Up Magazines

The pin-up magazine began with 'La Vie Parisienne' in the Victorian era when the pictures were drawn.

Collectors prefer the artwork pin-up and especially look for superb covers like the ones designed for pre-war American magazines by Dryben and Bolles. The lingerie shots found in magazines like 'Spick', 'Span' and 'Silky' are also very popular. One of the most sought after artists is Pett, the man who created Jane of the 'Daily Mirror' and examples of his work turn up from time to time.

Carnival Summer Special, 1956.   £4

Movie Merry-Go-Round, 1937. £10

Mayfair, 1st Issue August 1966.   £45

Flirty, a Fresh Magazine by **Revista De Paraiso**.   £6

Health & Efficiency, The National Sunbathing Magazine, October 1935.   £5

Wink, A Whirl of a Girl, Silk Stockings and High Heels. £10

Masque, 1950's Fetish Magazine.   £15

Pin Up Magazines

Left

The Stocking Parade, 1938.
£12
Spick, 1970. £6
Beautiful Britons, 1st Issue, 1955. £10
QT The Best of Beauty, 1958. £6
Charm, 1950's. £3
Handies Silk Stocking Revue, 1936. £12
Gay French Life, 1930's. £6
Span, 1956. £5
Paris Music Hall, 1932. £12
(Yesterday's Paper)

Right

Blighty, The National Humorous Weekly, Jan 1953. £2
Fiesta, 1957. £3
Racy Stories by **Utopia Publications**, 1950's. £12
Snappy Stories by **Utopia Publications**, 1950's. £12
Harlem Hotspots by **Utopia Publications**, 1950's. £12
La Vie Parisienne, 1928. £12
French Art & Models, 1930's. £10
Pussy Cat, 1960's. £6
Paris Magazine, 1949. £4
(Yesterday's Paper)

(Yesterday's Paper)

Pin Up Magazines

(Yesterday's Paper)

Pin Up Magazines

Film Fun, 1936. £12
Penthouse, The Magazine for
Men, 1st Issue, 1965. £15
Razzle, March 1935. £5
Movie Humor, 1935. £10
Gay Book Magazine, 1937. £8
Real Screen Fun, June 1937.£8

(Yesterday's Paper)

Postcards

The postcard boom began in Britain in 1870 and early ones were designed to take the address on one side and the message and illustration on the other. These cards came complete with a half penny stamp and were seized on as the ideal way of keeping in touch with friends at a low cost. It was not till 1894 that cards were produced for use with an adhesive stamp and in 1902 the vogue for pretty postcards really took off when an Act of Parliament was passed allowing the message and address to be written on the same side.

A set of six **Furness Railway** official postcards. £300

Raphael Tuck card **'The Jade Shawl'**. £40

Souvenir de France, woven silk postcard, 1914. £12

Early aviation postcard **'ICS Student Robert Slack'**. £20

Count Zeppelin in his Airship, Zeppelin III. £20

In Memoriam Titanic 1912. £35

(Paul Sheppard)

Postcards

Language of Flowers postcard.
£3

French political card.
£8

German humorous card **'Devil is that all'**, Series 163.
£8

German Bathing Beauties, by **S. Hildesheimer**, 1903.
£8

'Tender Thoughts hereby Expressed'.
£15

Bloomers, French saucy postcard.
£6

I Saw These Last Night, Are They Yours?
£5

'Oh Emil your kisses are so wet today', German.
£10

An early glamour card with attached hair.
£10

(Paul Sheppard)

Postcards

1930's humorous postcard **'The Voyage was Glorious But...'**. £8

French novelty card **'Voyage Sensationnel'**, 1907. £20

Parisienne Stocking study with **Pierrot** doll. £8

Taking it easy at Llandudno, with pull out views, 1915. £15

Something for you from Clevedon. £15

German chromo litho fantasy card **'One way to keep her quiet'**. £15

Les P'tites Femmes by **F. Fabiano** £12

Fry's Five Boys, take off postcard, 1909. £5

Alpha series fantasy postcard, **Un Bon Vivant**, 1905. £15

(Paul Sheppard)

Postcards

Saint Galmier Source Badoit, French card, 1908. £8

1960's European 3D postcard. £3

Map showing the course of the **Truelove River**. £5

The Disastrous Fire at Harrow School, 1908. £10

An early Manchester postcard, unillustrated, 1900. £20

Set of **Southwold railway** postcards. £50

The **Austin A30 'You can depend on it.'** £6

Barnes shop front **'Bananas are Best'**. £15

(Paul Sheppard)

Postcards

Louis Wain cat postcard   £10

The **Caledonian Railway Company's Central Station Hotel, Glasgow**.   £5

Hands Across the Sea, R.M.S. Empress of Britain, woven silk postcard.   £25

Camp Silhouette card **'Lights Out'**.   £12

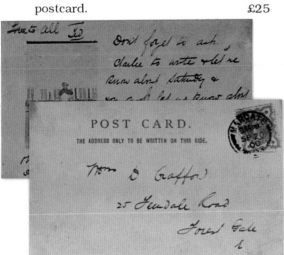

An early postcard with real photographs affixed to back, 1900.   £20

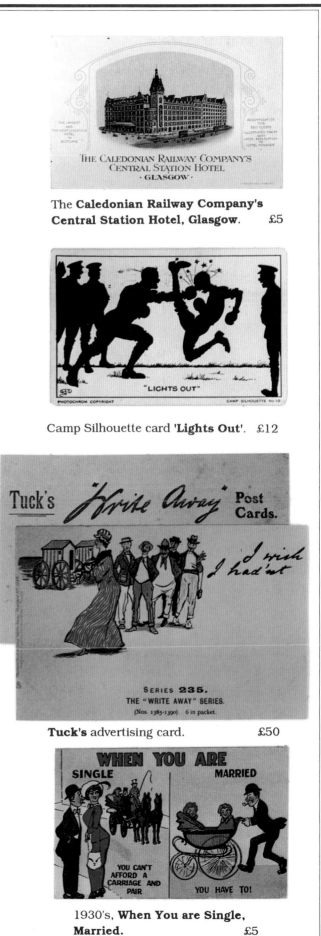

Tuck's advertising card.   £50

Destruction of the Memorial Theatre, Stratford, 1926.   £25

1930's, When You are Single, Married.   £5

(Paul Sheppard)

Postcards

Shirley Temple real photograph, hand coloured. £5

German **Art Deco** postcard. £15

My photograph, 'Eye hath Not Seen It'. £5

Falconer matt finish glamour card 'She stoops to conquer'. £8

Raphael Tuck's 'Coon Kids' postcard **'We'se Out Sportin'**.£4

Alpha series fantasy postcard, **'Tête De Mort'**, 1905. £15

If not muzzled her tongue would run away from her. £8

No wonder there are so many accidents. £5

German chromo litho, humorous card, **S.B. series**. £15

(Paul Sheppard)

Quilts

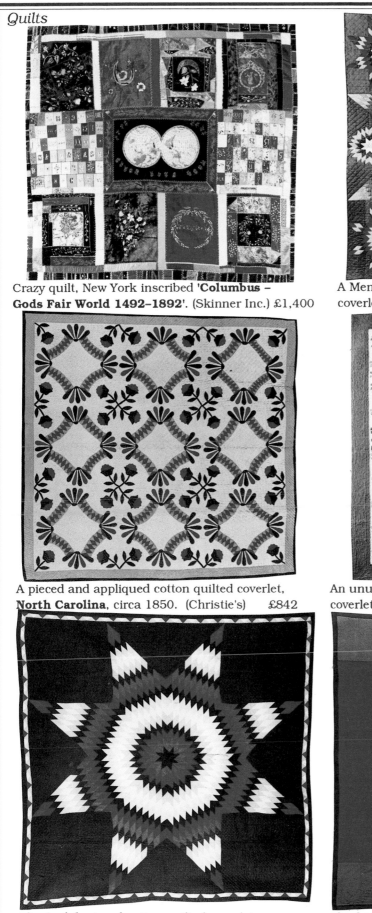

Crazy quilt, New York inscribed **'Columbus – Gods Fair World 1492–1892'**. (Skinner Inc.) £1,400

A Mennonite pieced and appliqued cotton quilted coverlet, **Pennsylvania**. (Christie's) £1,750

A pieced and appliqued cotton quilted coverlet, **North Carolina**, circa 1850. (Christie's) £842

An unusual appliqued and embroidered cotton coverlet, **Nazareth**, 1932. (Christie's) £23,500

An **Amish** pieced cotton quilted coverlet, Pennysylvania, circa 1930. (Christie's) £6,000

An **Amish** pieced wool quilted coverlet, Lancaster County, circa 1920. (Christie's) £1,500

Quilts

American mid 19th century pieced and appliqued cotton **Album** quilt. (Skinner) £6,000

A pieced and appliqued quilted cotton coverlet, **American**, mid 19th century. (Christie's) £2,550

A rare **Amish** cotton quilted coverlet, **Lancaster County, Pennysylvania**. (Christie's) £6,000

A wool and cotton quilted coverlet, **American**, 19th century, 75in. x 76in. (Christie's) £4,500

An important appliqued and stuffed **Album** quilt, **Baltimore**. (Christie's) £75,500

A pieced cotton quilted coverlet, **American**, 19th century, 72in. x 84$^{1}/_{2}$in. (Christie's) £1,750

Radios and Televisions

Ferranti 7 valve Superheterodyne radio, Model A1 in a figured walnut Art Deco style case, 1932, 19in. high. £350

1950's Echo Portable Mains radio model V122 in a green plastic case, 9in. high. £65

A 1930's Ultra 25 A16A radio in a polished walnut Art Deco style case with chromium plate embellishments, 20in. high. £200

Ferranti Nova Super H.E.T. radio in a brown bakelite case, 18in. high. £350

An **R.C.A. Victor Yachtsman, Marine/Aircraft receiver** in a green plastic case, 9in. high. £45

Ballantine's Whisky Bottle radio complete with original box, 9in. high, circa 1965. £25

(Paul Spindley)

117

Radios and Televisions

Left
Westminster radio set Model P.W.R.2., in a brown bakelite case, 12in. high.   £65
Bush D.A.C. 90 radio, circa 1950, in a white plastic case, 9¹/₂in. high.   £100
Ferguson 208V radio in a figured walnut case, 9in. high.
                                        £45

1930's Philips Type 701AX free standing radio in a figured walnut case, 39in. high.   £450

1930's Echo A21 radio in a brown bakelite case, 19in. high.
                                        £300

Ferguson Model 503 AC Main radio, 1930's in a figured walnut case, 22in. high.   £250

(Paul Spindley)

Radios and Televisions

Right

Stewart Warner 1920's model 300 radio set complete with 415 speaker, 21in. high. £400

Emor Globe radio, circa 1947 in a chrome plated case and black metal stand, 43in. high. £900

U.S.S.R. Spidola radio set in plastic case, circa 1964, 8in. high. £30

Decca battery radio in a round yellow plastic case, Model TPW7, 10^1/$_2$in. high. £45

Bakelite cased Bush TV 22 with 8in. screen, circa 1950. £175

A Philco 444 radio, 15in. high. £225

1930's Marconi radio Model 264A in a polished walnut Art Deco style case with chromium plate embellishments, 18in. high. £250

(Paul Spindley)

Radios and Televisions

1930's American radio in a brown bakelite case, 7in. high. £75

K.B. Kolster Brandes Ltd, **radio** in an ivory coloured plastic case, 7in. high. £75

A **Bush D.A.C. 10 Radio**, 8in high. £75

Skymaster Transistor Portable Radio, circa 1960, 7in. high. £20

Radio Rentals Group radio in a white plastic case, 9in. high. £45

Bush 1950's portable battery radio in plastic case, 11in. high. £30

An Australian produced **Healing radio Model SOIE, Golden Voice**, in a brown bakelite case, 15in. high. £75

Philips Superinductance 4 valve model 830A radio, 19in. high, 1930's. £350

Pilot Superheterodyne radio Model U650 in a figured walnut case, 19^{1}/$_{2}$in. high, 1930's. £300

(Paul Spindley)

Railway Memorabilia

There is a positive passion for collecting anything connected with trains and railways from cups and saucers that saw service in dining cars to station signs and even whole trains. This is a manifestation of the enthusiasm that the public has shown toward the train ever since the first public railway was opened between Stockton and Darlington in 1825. By 1900 there were over two hundred railway companies operating in Britain so there is a wealth of items to be collected over the length and breadth of the land. People seek out tickets, timetables, train number plates, maps, clocks, lamp standards and even the brass locks from train lavatory doors. Train nameplates are an especially thriving area. Most of the railway companies produced beautiful posters and photographed views of the countryside which were displayed in railway carriages and these too are eagerly collected.

Railway Jubilee Commemoration plate, 1875. £100

North British Railway Official Tourist Guide. £50

A **Midland Railway** tin tea caddie. £100

Great Northern Railway Parcels Rate Book, Leicester. £40

A **GWR** official publication, 'A **GWR** signal box'. £40

A **North Eastern Railway** station lamp. £250

(Sheffield Railwayana Auctions)

121

Railway Memorabilia

London Midland & Scottish Railway hand brush. £30

A rare **Pullman Car Company** Guide. £150

Caedu Crossing Brynmenyn single line key. £75

Rare cast iron wagon plate **W.R. Renshaw & Co.**, 1902. £60

A **GWR** enamel Trespass sign. £150

Copper tea urn from **Wolferton Royal Station**. £150

(Sheffield Railwayana Auctions)

Railway Memorabilia

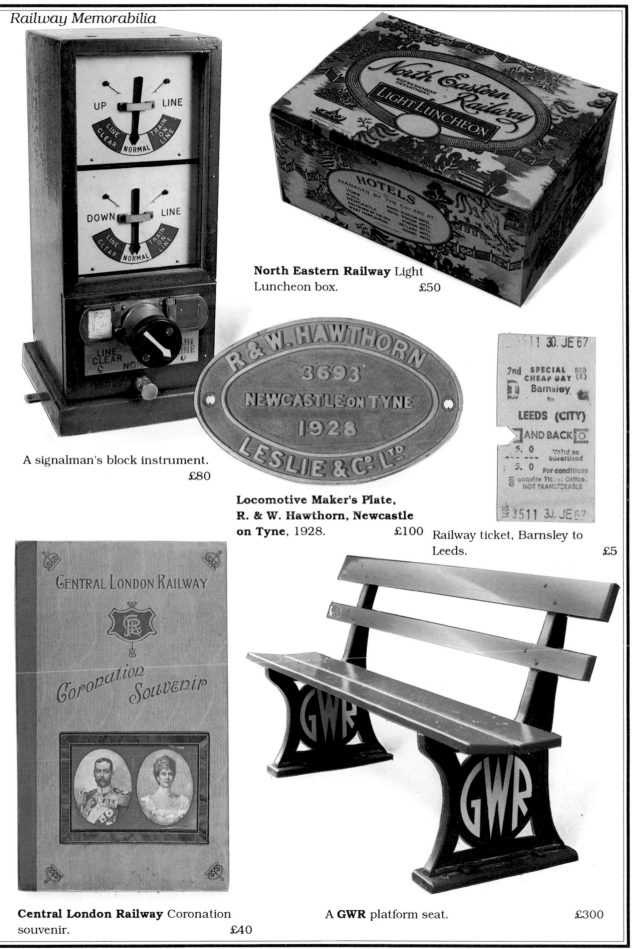

North Eastern Railway Light
Luncheon box.   £50

A signalman's block instrument.
£80

**Locomotive Maker's Plate,
R. & W. Hawthorn, Newcastle
on Tyne**, 1928.   £100

Railway ticket, Barnsley to
Leeds.   £5

Central London Railway Coronation
souvenir.   £40

A **GWR** platform seat.   £300

(Sheffield Railwayana Auctions)

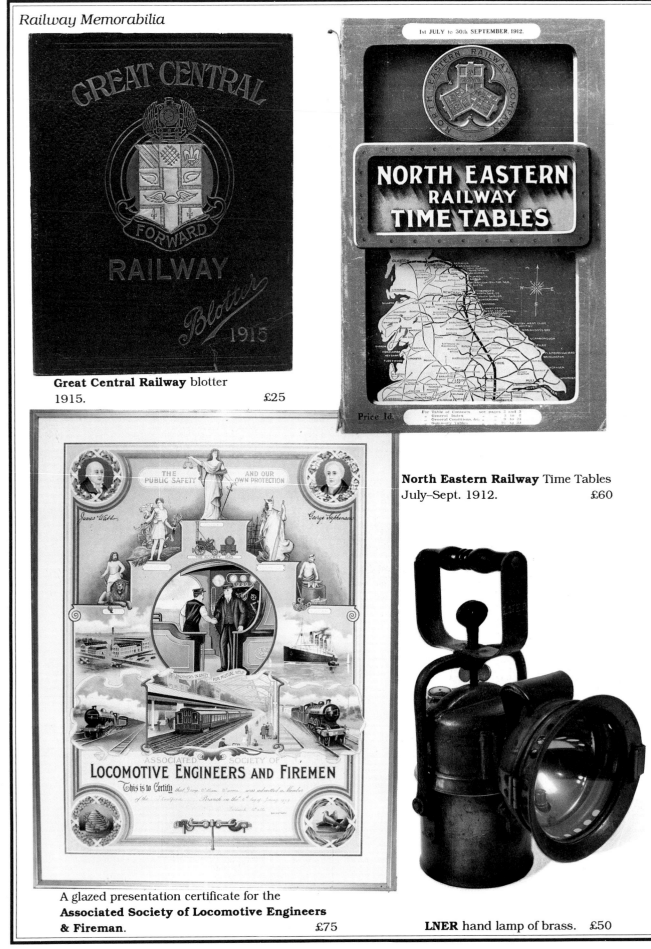

Railway Memorabilia

Great Central Railway blotter
1915.   £25

North Eastern Railway Time Tables
July–Sept. 1912.   £60

A glazed presentation certificate for the
**Associated Society of Locomotive Engineers
& Fireman.**   £75

LNER hand lamp of brass.   £50

(Sheffield Railwayana Auctions)

Railway Memorabilia

South Eastern Railways clock in a mahogany case.   £350

GWR cast iron wagon sign.   £50

L & NWR padlock.   £7

London Tilbury & Southend Railway bucket.   £100

Railway brassed handlamp, **'Pitcaple'**.   £100

Glasgow and South Western railway chamber pot.   £125

(Sheffield Railwayana Auctions)

Railway Memorabilia

Railway station master's peaked cap.   £50

A **London and North Western Railway** guard's acetylene headlamp.   £60

A **LNER** A.R.P. warden's rattle to warn of gas attack.   £40

Signal Box instrument from **Wellend Bank, Spalding**.   £40

A **Belfast and County Down Railway** enamel armband.   £40

Hadham station sign.   £150

The **Glasgow and South Western Railway** Time Tables.   £75

Locomotive Maker's Plate, Peckett & Sons, Bristol 1923.   £150

(Sheffield Railwayana Auctions)

Railway Memorabilia

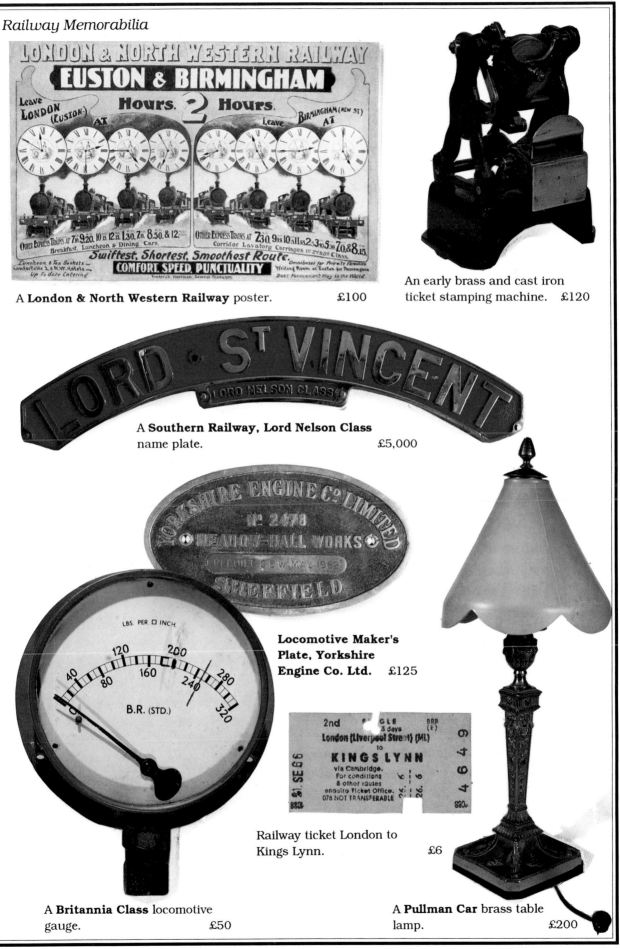

A **London & North Western Railway** poster. £100

An early brass and cast iron ticket stamping machine. £120

A **Southern Railway, Lord Nelson Class** name plate. £5,000

Locomotive Maker's Plate, Yorkshire Engine Co. Ltd. £125

Railway ticket London to Kings Lynn. £6

A **Britannia Class** locomotive gauge. £50

A **Pullman Car** brass table lamp. £200

(Sheffield Railwayana Auctions)

Railway Memorabilia

London & South Western Time Tables
1907–1908. £70

Midland & Great Northern Joint
Railway armband. £60

Locomotive Maker's Plate, Beyer,
Peacock & Co. Ltd., 1956. £100

LNER poster 'The Palace of Holyrood'. £150

Lancashire & Yorkshire
Railway half pint beer
bottle. £25

(Sheffield Railwayana Auctions)

Railway Memorabilia

LNER complimentary fan. £50

Bassett-Lowke model locomotive catalogue. £30

A **Southern Railway**, **King Arthur Class** name plate. £4,000

A **LNER** 'Cathedral' series dessert plate. £60

A rare cigarette vending machine. £400

An **LMS** outdoor porter's armband. £40

A rare **GWR** Guide to golf courses 1937. £100

(Sheffield Railwayana Auctions)

129

Railway Memorabilia

British Rail leather wages cash bag. £30

Locomotive Maker's Plate, Hyde Park Works 1918. £100

Cast iron coach plate **GNR, Doncaster.** £40

South Eastern & Chatham Railway Time Tables Oct. 1910. £60

A rare enamel sign for **Rhymney Railway 'Fire Buckets'.** £500

GWR stoneware ginger beer bottle. £250

(Sheffield Railwayana Auctions)

130

Rock & Pop Posters

The 'Swinging Sixties' and the 1970's were the era of flower-power, the hippies, call it what you will. The period saw the upsurge of a new pop culture, the stars of which often enjoyed a cult status and a devotion bordering on idolatry. It was at this time too that cannabis, LSD and other 'mind-blowing' drugs began to be widely used and the word 'psychedelic' entered common parlance. It is this word which probably best describes the typical posters of the period, which were eagerly collected and formed a major decorative feature in most 'with-it' rooms.

Sopwith Camel, Matrix, San Francisco, 14in. x 20in., 1967. £100

Sly and The Family Stone, Winterland, San Francisco, December 1969, 14in. x 22in. £85

The Invisible Circus, Glide Church, San Francisco, 1967, 20in. x 14^1/$_2$in. £20

Jefferson Airplane, Avalon Ballroom, San Francisco, July 1966, 15in. x 21in. £75

'Isle of Wight Festival' poster by **David Roe**, 1970. (Dave Lewis) £45

(Christopher Baglee Style Collection)

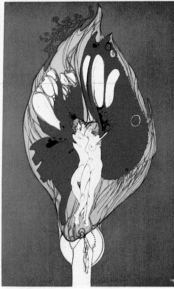

The Daily Flash, Avalon Ballroom, San Francisco, May 1966, 14¹/₂in. x 20in. £35

Love Moths in a Candle Flame, psychedelic image poster, 14in. x 22in., 1967. £40

Mister Tambourine Man, poster for **Bob Dylan** by **Martin Sharp**, 1967. £65

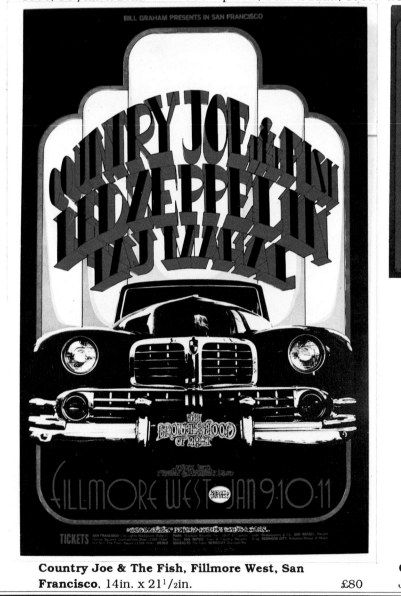

Michael McClure's The Beard, Freeborn Hall, University of California, April 1966. £30

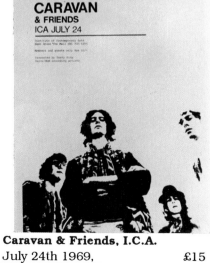

Country Joe & The Fish, Fillmore West, San Francisco, 14in. x 21¹/₂in. £80

Caravan & Friends, I.C.A. July 24th 1969, £15

(Christopher Baglee Style Collection)

Rock & Pop Posters

**Stoneground at the Whisky
A-Go-Go, Hollywood,**
14in. x 18¹/₂in., 1972.   £75

Future Shock poster 1984,
16¹/₂in. x 11¹/₂in.   £5

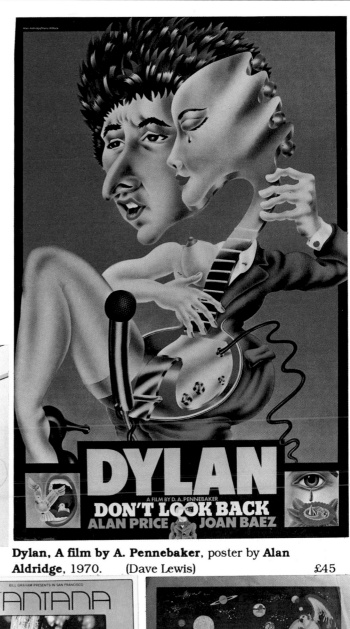

Dylan, A film by A. Pennebaker, poster by **Alan
Aldridge**, 1970.   (Dave Lewis)   £45

**The Hells Angels present Big
Brother and The Holding Co.,
California Hall, San Francisco,**
Feb 1967, 14¹/₂in. x 20in.   £40

**Santana, Winterland, San
Francisco** 1969,
14in. x 22in.   £85

A is for Apple, promotional
poster designed by **The Fool
Group** for the **Beatles,**
1967.   £60

(Christopher Baglee Style Collection)

Rock & Pop Posters

Imagine, John Lennon Peace Calendar, 1972. £50

P.H. Phactor Blues Band, 40 Cedar Alley, August 1966, £35

Crazy World of Arthur Brown, Liverpool Students Union, 1967, 12in. x 18in. £40

Sunshine Superman poster for **Donovan** by **Martin Sharp**. £65

Poster for **The Tube, Channel 4**, 16¹/₂in. x 23¹/₂in., 1982. £20

Psychedelic Art, First West Coast Show, 1967, £45

Country Joe and the Fish, Berkeley, February 1967. £50

Cosmic Car Show, Muir Beach, San Francisco, 1967. £60

Daily Flash, Avalon Ballroom, San Francisco, 1966, £75

(Christopher Baglee Style Collection)

Samplers

From the early 18th century young girls of leisured families were set to make a sampler when they were around ten years old as a sort of 'apprentice piece' to show their developing skill as needlewomen. The samplers were designed to display the various stitches which the girl could execute and they were laid out in stylised form incorporating the letters of the alphabet, the maker's name and age, sometimes the place where it was made and a stitched representation of the owner's home.

Rare needlework sampler, **Massachusetts**, 1799. (Skinner Inc.)   £19,270

Early 19th century sampler by **Margaret Fleming**, 1804. (Phillips)   £200

A fine and rare needlework sampler, **Norwich, Connecticut**, 1774. (Christie's)   £31,132

A needlework silk on linen sampler, **Scituate, Massachusetts**, 1804. (Christie's)   £3,828

A fine needlework sampler, probably **Marblehead, Massachusetts**, 1805. (Christie's)   £14,396

Sanitary Samples

We are so used to 'mod. cons.' today that it is hard to imagine what an exciting innovation modern plumbing must have been when it was first introduced, and the salesman, with his samples of toilets and basins which would seem totally prosaic to us, would have been something of a trailblazer. The Victorians, of course, wasted no time in ensuring such items were floridly decorated in the taste of the period!

Salesman's samples of a Victorian multicoloured floral toilet set. £250 each

Salesman's samples of a toilet and pedestal basin, 1930's, 5in. high. £25

Victorian salesman's sample of multicoloured floral wash basin, 9in. x 6in. £275

Shop counter or window display sample of a **Puritas Washdown Closet** with floral decoration, late 19th century. £275

Junkers shower bath novelty sample of Polish origin, 7in. tall. £30

1930's salesman's sample toilets by **de Sphinx of Holland, Alfred Johnson & Sons** and **Royal Doulton**. £25 each

(Dave Lewis)

Scent Bottles

In Victorian times the lady of fashion carried a double ended, overlay scent bottle in her reticule but it was the glass masters of the early 20th century who sold the idea of individually designed bottles to perfume manufacturers and René Lalique made a profitable speciality of designing bottles for Coty and Nina Ricci among others. His elegant bottles helped sell the scent inside and other manufacturers eagerly followed his lead, employing artists like Daum, Gallé and Webb to design scent bottles which have survived as pieces of beauty in their own right.

A frosted glass scent bottle modelled as **Bonzo the Dog**, 2³/₄in. high.
(Christie's)   £66

'Volubilis', an **Art Deco** perfume bottle and stopper, moulded in relief with flowers and foliage, 4¹/₂in. high.
(Christie's S. Ken.)   £495

'Dans La Nuit', a **Lalique** spherical scent bottle and stopper, made for **Worth**, 3in. high.
(Christie's)   £198

'Pluie D'Or', a **Baccarat** enamelled clear bottle for **A. Gravier**, of triangular section, 5³/₄in.
(Bonhams)   £4,200

'Voltigy', a **Baccarat** clear bottle for **A. Gravier**, modelled as a butterfly with outstretched wings, 3¹/₂in.
(Bonhams)   £18,000

'Le Nouveau Gardenia', a **Lalique** clear glass perfume bottle and stopper for **Coty**, 13.6cm. high.
(Phillips)   £2,300

'Hantise', a **Baccarat** black enamelled pink opaque bottle for **A. Gravier**, 4¹/₂in.
(Bonhams)   £3,400

'Malice', a **Baccarat** enamelled clear bottle for **A. Gravier**, of squared baluster form, 4¹/₂in.
(Bonhams)   £1,800

'Cactus', A **Lalique** frosted glass scent bottle and stopper moulded in relief with nodes enamelled in black, 4in. high. (Christie's)   £200

A **Gallé** carved, acid etched and cased glass flaçon and stopper, 11.2cm. high.
(Christie's)   £2,860

Scent Bottles

'Fougères', a **Lalique** clear glass scent bottle and stopper, moulded in relief with an oval green stained panel, 9.2cm. high.
(Phillips)   £4,830

Glass scent spray with chromium fittings, 1930's.
(Muir Hewitt)   £35

'Sans Adieu', a **Lalique** emerald green scent bottle and stopper made for **Worth**.
(Christie's)   £132

A **Cristallerie de Pantin** cameo brûle-parfum, the yellow opalescent body overlaid in pink, 6in. high.
(Christie's S. Ken.) £550

'La Joie D'Aimer', a **Baccarat** enamelled clear bottle for **A. Gravier**, of octagonal form, 5¹/₄in.
(Bonhams)   £1,400

1930's scent bottle in the form of a crinolined lady, with black stopper.   £20

'Me Voici', a **Baccarat** enamelled clear bottle for **A. Gravier**, of shoe form, with faceted stopper, 4in. wide.
(Bonhams) £6,200

A **Louis XVI** gold-mounted glass scent-flask, the front applied with an oval vari-colour gold medallion, Paris 1777–78, 4in. long.
(Christie's)   £1,320

'Quatre Soleils', a **Lalique** amber-tinted scent bottle and stopper, 7.2cm. high.
(Christie's)   £14,300

A gilt metal cased glass scent bottle and stopper made for **Rolex**, 2in. long.
(Christie's)   £300

A 1930's Eau de Cologne bottle with green glass stopper.

'Sans Adieu', a **Lalique** Art Deco green glass perfume bottle for **Worth**, 10.9cm. high.
(Phillips)   £550

Scraps

Originally from Germany scraps, or
Oblaten, are highly coloured,
stylised paper cut-outs. They
became popular and were used
throughout Europe and America for
decorative purposes.

Edward VII, $8^1/_4$in. x $7^1/_4$in.   £10
Cherub with flowers,
$4^3/_4$in. x $2^1/_2$in.   £3
Home Sweet Home,
$2^1/_2$in. x $6^3/_4$in.   £4
Little Red Riding Hood,
8in. x $3^1/_2$in.   £8
Boy with ball, $9^1/_2$in. x $2^1/_2$in. £6
Two schoolboys, 4in. x 3in.   £3
Pigs at school, 4in. x 7in.   £8

(Ute Twite)

Scraps

Girl with dog, 6in. x 5in. £8
Boy with flower baskets,
$3^3/_4$in. x $3^1/_2$in. £4
Battleship, 5in. x 3in. £4
Fast Asleep, 3in. x 5in. £3
Scottie Dog, $2^1/_2$in. x $2^1/_4$in. £2
Thine in Truth, thine in love,
$1^1/_2$in. x 2in. £2
Hand with violets,
$6^3/_4$in. x $2^1/_2$in. £3
Fireman, $6^3/_4$in. x $2^1/_2$in. £6
As happy as a King,
7in. x $9^1/_2$in. £10

(Ute Twite)

Scraps

Dancing Cat, 6³/₄in. x 3in. £5
Kitten in a basket,
2¹/₄in. x 3³/₄in. £3
Hold Tight printed by **W.D. &
S.**, No. 321, 9³/₄in. x 7³/₄in. £8
Cherub on a cloud,
4¹/₄in. x 3¹/₄in. £4
Girl with a garland of roses,
6¹/₂in. x 4¹/₄in. £7
Lady with flowers in her hair,
3in. x 1³/₄in. £3
Boy with flowers,
6¹/₄in. x 2¹/₄in. £3
Girl with roses,
6¹/₄in. x 2¹/₄in. £3
Alphabetical characters,
6in. x 5in. £8

(Ute Twite)

Scraps

Flowers, $5^1/_2$in. x $3^1/_2$in.   £3
Girl with feathered hat,
$4^1/_2$in. x $3^1/_2$in.   £4
Clown and Ass,
$4^3/_4$in. x $5^1/_2$in.   £8
Children in a basket,
$3^1/_2$in. x $2^1/_2$in.   £5
Kitten in a shoe,
$2^1/_2$in. x $3^1/_2$in.   £3
Our Old Friend,
7in. x $2^1/_2$in.   £8
**John Bull and the British
Bulldog**, $5^1/_2$in. x $2^3/_4$in.   £5
Lucky Tub, 4in. x $8^3/_4$in.   £8

(Ute Twite)

Song Sheets

Among earlier items of sheet music, those which make the best prices are the ones with elaborate and colourful Victorian lithographed covers from the era of the music hall.

When the Waltz Was Through by Archie Gottler. £4

Clown Songs by **Tom Matthews**, dated 1856. £12

Champagne Charlie by **George Leybourne**. £12

Jessie, The Belle at the Bar by **George Ware**. £12

(Dave Lewis)

Song Sheets

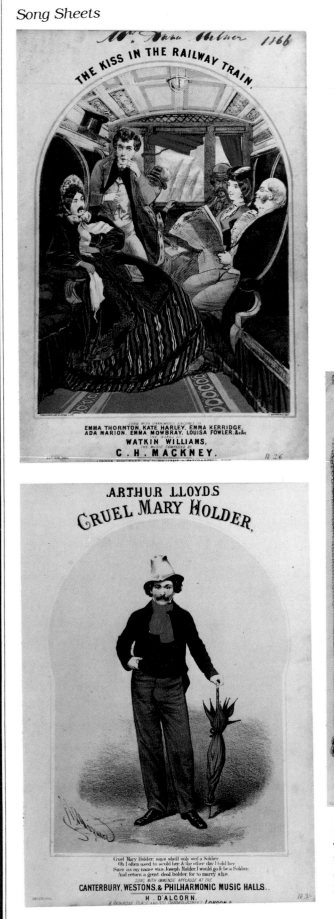

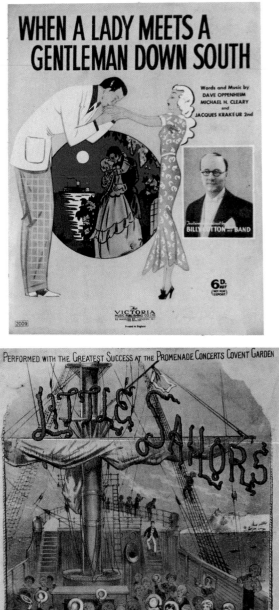

The Kiss in the Railway Train by **C.H. Mackney,** dated 1866. £12

When a Lady Meets a Gentleman Down South by **Dave Oppenheim.** £4

Cruel Mary Holder by **Arthur Lloyd.** £12

Little Sailors by **A.G. Crowe.** £12

(Dave Lewis)

Song Sheets

Sweet Linnet by **Downing Evans Esq**. £6
The English, Irish & Scotchman or Paddy's Wish by **George Ware**. £12
She's a Good Good Girl! by **Billy Milton**. £4
Felix Kept on Walking, sheet music by **E.D. Bryant**, 1933. £8

(Dave Lewis)

Tobacco Tins

It is hardly surprising that tobacco tins should be such popular collectables. Often brightly coloured and beautifully designed, they have the added advantage of being durable, and are quite often to be found full of nails, washers or whatever, lurking in garages and garden sheds.

They first became widely used during the 1860s, and examples from this time usually had the labels pasted on the lid, as well as, quite often, on the inside of the lid. As colour printing techniques improved, these labels became ever more attractive, and played a significant role in glamorising the brand they contained. By the 1890s most has the image printed directly on to the top, which further improved the quality.

By 1881 there were 570 licensed tobacco manufacturers, so there is a plentiful range to collect. Some of the rarer ones to look out for are Taddy, Lusby and Kriegsfeld.

Player's Navy Cut Cigarettes. £20

Taddy & Co's Myrtle Grove Cigarettes. £125

Lambert & Butler 'May Blossom Cigarettes', 1890. £10

Ogden's Redbreast Flake. £20

W.D. & H.O. Wills 'Gold Flake' tin, 6in. wide. £15

Tam O''Shanter Tobacco, by Stephen Mitchell & Son, Glasgow, printed tin manufactured by Robert Gibson & Sons Ltd., Manchester, $8^1/2$in. wide. £25

(Dave Lewis)

Tobacco Tins

Lambert & Butler's Gold Leaf Honeydew Cigarettes. £15

'Carrolls, Mick McQuaid Cut Plug', tobacco tin manufactured by P.J. Carroll & Co. Ltd., Dublin, Cork, London, Glasgow, 7in. x 3in. £35

Ogden's Redbreast Flake. £25

'Bond of Union Smoking Mixture'. £25

Cope's Navy Cut Cigarettes. £30

Gallaher's Rich Dark Honeydew. £25

Afrikander Flake, printed tin, 1930's. £15

McDonald's Kilty Brand Cut Golden Bar. £25

Pritchard & Burtons 'Boar's Head Tobacco' in printed tin, 4in. diameter. £3

Hignett's Cavalier Brand Bright Flake. £25

Hignett's Pilot Flake. £35

Ogden's Walnut Plug tobacco tin. £5

(Dave Lewis)

Toilets

The water closet was invented in 1805 by Joseph Bramah but it was some years before the idea really caught on.

The system operated through a leadlined wooden cased cistern which was, in time, replaced by an ornate cast iron version and eventually by a ceramic one.

The lavatory bowls were ceramic and some of the better ones were decorated. The Victorians really took to this transfer-printed ware during the last quarter of the 19th century. As a rule, this decoration is based on a floral pattern, usually in blue and white, though multi-coloured specimens do appear on the market from time to time. The toilet bowl was usually bought en suite with a washbasin and sometimes with a bath.

The best known manufacturers were Doulton, Shanks and Pauls.

The Simplicitas Patent Closet with Dahlia floral decoration, circa 1890.   £300

Doulton & Co. London Closet fitted with **Doultons Patent Metallo Keramic Joint**, circa 1900.   £300

The Continental made by **Baxendale & Co. Edinburgh, Liverpool & Manchester** with floral decoration.   £350

The Dee Wash Down Closet with floral decoration circa 1900.   £300

Twyfords Unitas 'Patent after flush' chamber dated 1888, with all over Dahlia floral design.   £300

(Dave Lewis)

Toilets

Shank's Patent Syphonic Closet decorated with blue floral displays, circa 1890. £300

Shield Wash Down Closet distributed by Fairclough, Manchester with blue floral design. £300

The Sanitas Wash Down Closet made in Stoke-on-Trent, circa 1902. £300

Invictas sepia transferred floral washdown Closet, circa 1895, manufactured by **Johnson Bros.** £300

The Simplicitas Patent Closet made by **Doulton & Co., Lambeth**, circa 1892. £350

Trent Sanitary Closet with Bullrush design, reg. no. 201590, circa 1885. £300

(Dave Lewis)

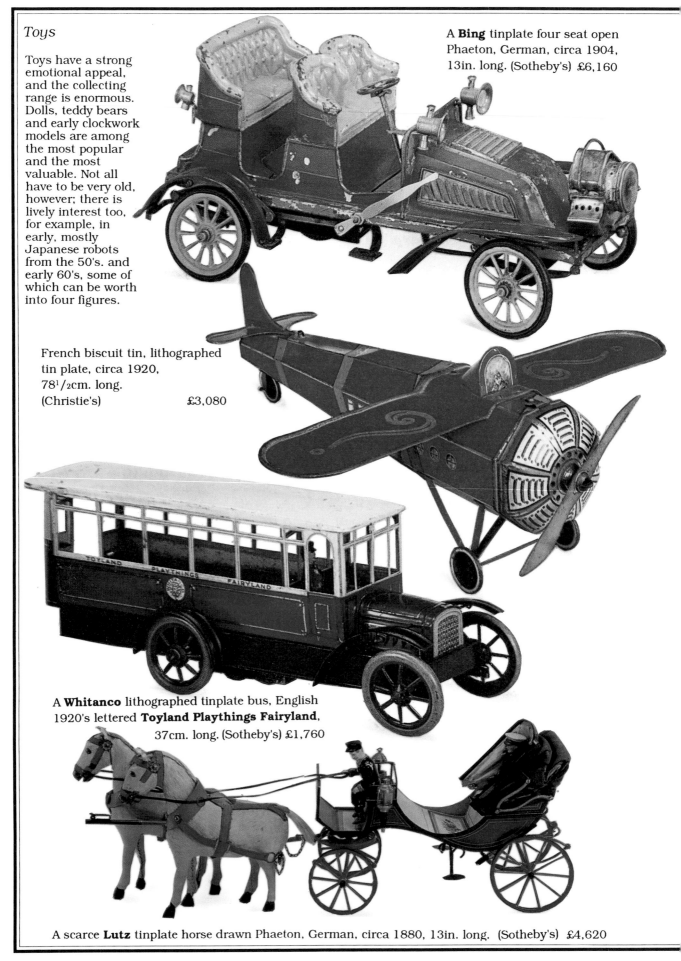

Toys

Toys have a strong emotional appeal, and the collecting range is enormous. Dolls, teddy bears and early clockwork models are among the most popular and the most valuable. Not all have to be very old, however; there is lively interest too, for example, in early, mostly Japanese robots from the 50's. and early 60's, some of which can be worth into four figures.

A **Bing** tinplate four seat open Phaeton, German, circa 1904, 13in. long. (Sotheby's) £6,160

French biscuit tin, lithographed tin plate, circa 1920, 78¹/₂cm. long. (Christie's)   £3,080

A **Whitanco** lithographed tinplate bus, English 1920's lettered **Toyland Playthings Fairyland**, 37cm. long. (Sotheby's) £1,760

A scarce **Lutz** tinplate horse drawn Phaeton, German, circa 1880, 13in. long. (Sotheby's) £4,620

Toys

An early **Donald Duck** puppet made from plaster, made by **Munzberg**, 1937, £1,850

A very rare short red plush teddy bear called **Alfonzo** with **Steiff** button, 13in. high, 1906. (Christie's) £12,100

Tinplate clockwork **Mickey Mouse** barrel organ toy, German, circa 1930, 8¼in. high. £1,300

A rare 1960's **Jupiter Robot the Space Explorer** by **Yonezawa**. £3,000

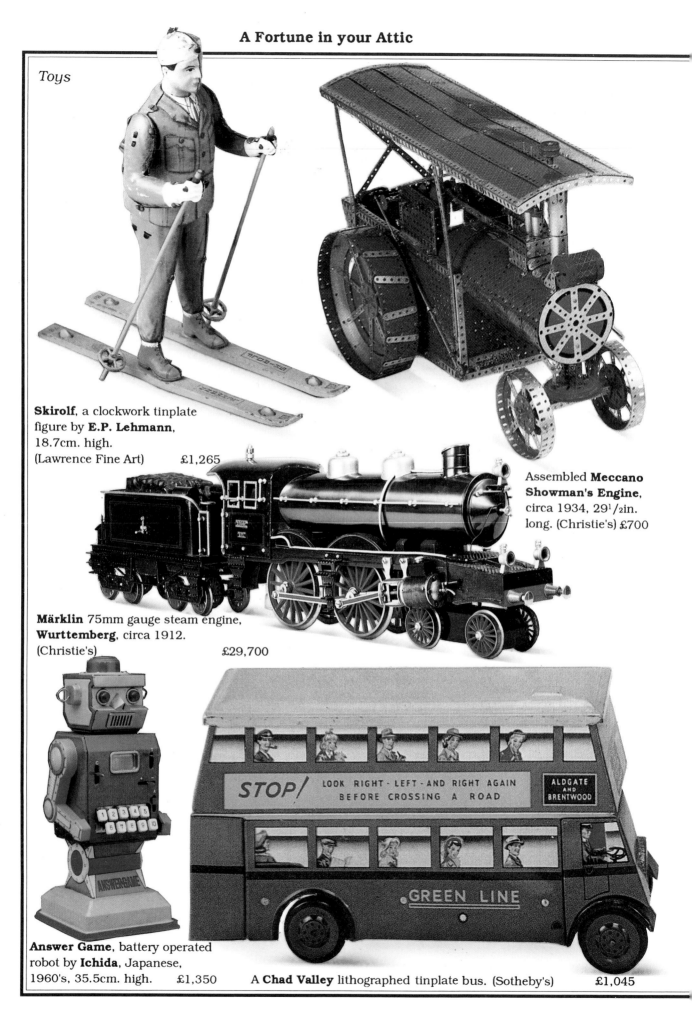

Toys

Skirolf, a clockwork tinplate figure by **E.P. Lehmann**, 18.7cm. high. (Lawrence Fine Art) £1,265

Assembled **Meccano Showman's Engine**, circa 1934, $29^1/_2$in. long. (Christie's) £700

Märklin 75mm gauge steam engine, **Wurttemberg**, circa 1912. (Christie's) £29,700

Answer Game, battery operated robot by **Ichida**, Japanese, 1960's, 35.5cm. high. £1,350

A **Chad Valley** lithographed tinplate bus. (Sotheby's) £1,045

Toys

A **Märklin** tinplate '**Aeropal**' hand or steam operated lighthouse roundabout, circa 1909, 19in. high. (Christie's) £12,100

A fine **Märklin** steam tinplate and iron fire pumper, circa 1900, 11in. long. (Christie's) £6,050

A **Nomura** Toys **Fokker Tri-motor** aeroplane, Japanese, 1930's, 14¹/₂in. long. (Sotheby's) £3,190

George Brown tinplate '**Charles**' hose reel, circa 1875, American, 23in. long. (Christie's) £127,050

A fine **Steiff** black mohair plush teddy bear, 1912, 19in. high. (Phillips) £8,000

153

Truncheons

Truncheons are the direct descendant of the basic club – even their name derives similarly to 'trunk'. We may think of them as being wielded principally by policemen, but they have also evolved into much more interesting forms, such as ceremonial batons and symbols of office. As such they can be very decorative, dated and initialled and carrying often a wealth of fascinating detail regarding their bearer's office. These are the ones which make really interesting and worthwhile collectables.

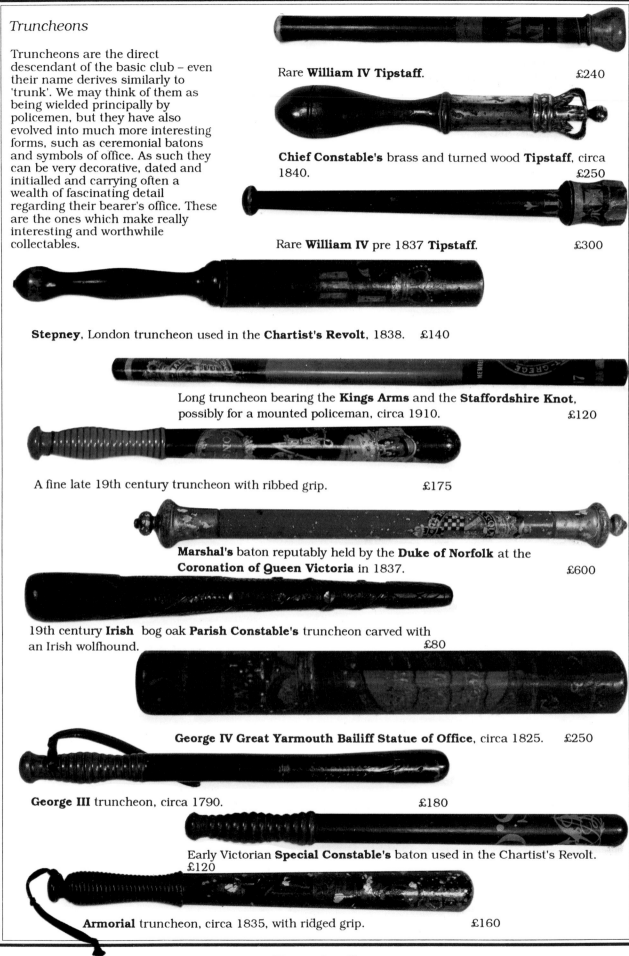

Rare **William IV Tipstaff**.   £240

Chief Constable's brass and turned wood **Tipstaff**, circa 1840.   £250

Rare **William IV** pre 1837 **Tipstaff**.   £300

Stepney, London truncheon used in the **Chartist's Revolt**, 1838.   £140

Long truncheon bearing the **Kings Arms** and the **Staffordshire Knot**, possibly for a mounted policeman, circa 1910.   £120

A fine late 19th century truncheon with ribbed grip.   £175

Marshal's baton reputably held by the **Duke of Norfolk** at the **Coronation of Queen Victoria** in 1837.   £600

19th century **Irish** bog oak **Parish Constable's** truncheon carved with an Irish wolfhound.   £80

George IV Great Yarmouth Bailiff Statue of Office, circa 1825.   £250

George III truncheon, circa 1790.   £180

Early Victorian **Special Constable's** baton used in the Chartist's Revolt.   £120

Armorial truncheon, circa 1835, with ridged grip.   £160

(George Court)

Valentine Cards

According to legend, St. Valentine's Day, 14th February, is the day that birds choose their mates....

Since the 15th century we have celebrated this day and communicated our feelings for one another through the customary practice of sending a gift or love token.

Valentine cards had been exchanged by lovers since the end of the 18th century but by 1835 the Post Office reported mailings of 60,000 on February 13th and after the introduction of the penny post in 1840, the number increased even more.

Victorian Valentine card, '**My love I send to the one I hold most dear**'. £15

To arms to Arms, ye British Brave. £25

Paper lace Valentine card with Love Birds. £20

Valentine greetings '**Though Walls Should Part Us**, 1921. £10

My Darling Still, Rememberest the Gladsome Time. £10

My love to you, litho printed card. £8

Long have I loved thee Truly, early 20th century Valentine card. £8

Oh what a St Valentines mug U.R. £6

Valentine Cards

To the one I love.   £8

Early 20th century folding Valentine card. £10

The wish of a Friend by **J.T. Wood**.   £15

My Comfort and my joy.   £5

Early French folding Valentine, 1907.   £15

To my Valentine.   £8

A Valentine Greeting.   £2

St. Valentine begs to remind you.   £8

Pressed paper folding Valentine.   £10

St. Valentine Greets You.   £6

(Yesterday's Paper)

Valentine Cards

Victorian pop-up Valentine card   £75

Forget me not for I'll remember thee, Victorian Valentine card.   £10

Fond Greetings to my Valentine.   £8

A Valentine for someone often in my thoughts.   £2

Language of Flowers, Youthful Innocence.   £6

To my own Valentine.   £6

I'm in love as you plainly may see.   £15

Early Victorian satirical Valentine card.   £25

(Yesterday's Paper)

Water Filters

As medical knowledge advanced, people became aware that many diseases were contracted by drinking impure water. By the 1830's therefore, carbon water filters had been developed for domestic use.

The earliest were fairly plain brown saltglazed affairs. Many companies produced them, but Doulton of Lambeth sprang to prominence by realising the potential for decorated wares. During the 1870's and 1880's two of Doulton's leading decorators, George Tinworth and Eliza Simmance, were responsible for many filters which became so ornate and attractive that they came in from the kitchen to sit on the dinner table of fashionable homes.

Doulton stoneware water filter with embossed floral decoration, 32cm. high. £400

Doulton stoneware water filter with floral decoration, 14^1/$_2$in. high. £400

Doulton stoneware water filter decorated with cherubs, 32cm. high. £400

Doulton siliconware water filter with embossed decoration, 33cm. high. £350

Doulton manganous carbon filter with brass tap, 35cm. high. £200

(Cyril Wickham)

Weathervanes

A moulded copper gilt bull weathervane attributed to **L.W. Cushing and Sons, Waltham, Massachusetts**, circa 1875.
(Christie's)   £3,086

A rare and important carved and gilded pine rooster weathervane, **Maine**, late 18th century, 28in. high.
(Sotheby's)   £39,699

An extremely rare American locomotive and tender copper weathervane, circa 1882, 61in. long.
(Skinner Inc.)   £115,625

A rare carved and painted weathervane in the form of a spotted hen, **New England**, 1850, 22¹/₄in. long.
(Christie's)   £12,342

A moulded copper and cast zinc horse weathervane by **A.L. Jewell and Co., Waltham, Massachusetts**, 1850, 17in. long. (Christie's) £2,525

Weathervanes

An extremely rare and important moulded
copper and zinc horse and rider weathervane by
**J. Howard and Company, West Bridgewater,
Massachusetts**, circa 1860, 76^{1}/$_{2}$in. high.
(Christie's)   £53,295